# Health by All Means
# Women Turning Structural Violence into Peace and Wellbeing

## Araceli Alonso and Teresa Langle de Paz

## DEEP ACTIVISM BOOK SERIES

This volume is the first of the Deep Activism Book Series under the auspices of the UW-Madison UNESCO Chair on Gender, Wellbeing and Culture of Peace

United Nations Educational, Scientific and Cultural Organization

UNESCO Chair on Gender, Wellbeing and a Culture of Peace University of Wisconsin-Madison,U.S.A.

Blue Mounds, Wisconsin, USA

**Deep Institute Online !**

www.deepinstitute.net

www.deepapproach.com

Certificate in Deep Education

ISBN   978-1-939755-43-8 (Paperback)

Library of Congress Cataloguing-in-Publication Data

1. Health, Women, Ethnography,

Keywords: Global health, women's health, wellbeing, community development, sustainable community health, feminist emotion, feminist theory, feminism.

Public: Health promotion, women's health

Cover: Painting by Natha Piña and photo by Teresa de Paz

# CONTENTS

## ACKNOWLEDGEMENTS

Writing the acknowledgements for this book has been the most difficult part of this process. Many individuals, many institutions, and many communities have been responsible for the success of the projects that have given birth to the pages we present here. First of all, we thank the Global Health Institute at the University of Madison-Wisconsin for sending Dr. Alonso to East Africa with a Travel Grant that became the foundation of her work with Health by Motorbike. Within the Global Health Institute, we want to express our most profound gratitude to Lori Diprete Brown for all those many "elevator talks" that provided fertile ground for learning and collaboration. We also thank the Department of Gender and Women's Studies at the University of Wisconsin-Madison for allowing bold ideas to grow and for opening up spaces to share different forms of knowledge. The encouragement of GWS colleagues and the support of Department Chairs Jane Collins, Judith Houck and Aili Tripp have been invaluable for the success of these projects and for the progression of this book.

Our recognition, admiration and gratitude go to the main characters of this book, the main protagonists of the success of the Health by All Means (HbAM) and of the Health by Motorbike (HbM) projects—the women from Kwale County, specifically from Lunga Lunga, Godo, Perani, Mpakani, Jirani, Umoja, Maasailand. The women, with the leadership and guidance of Bendettah Muthina Thomas and Josephine Matini have conceived an incredible and subversive movement towards sustainable health and wellbeing. None of the HbAM projects, however, would have been possible without the assistance of the invaluable and irreplaceable Hesperian Foundation Books; *Where Women Had*

*No Doctor* (2010) and A *Book for Midwives* (2010) were extraordinarily relevant for all—the women and the UW-Madison Team.

Our deepest appreciation goes to all the students who participated in this Global Health adventure, more than sixty students from 2010 to 2015; special thanks go to the student pioneers of 2010—Megan Kleber, Kelsey Bilek, Sarah Donohue, and Sofía Noguera who opened up many opportunities of community engagement for other prospect fellow students. Megan was also the genius and the engine for the design of the nonprofit organization; Megan took classes to train herself on non-profit development, met with lawyers, and prepared tons of paperwork that resulted in the foundation and launching of the NGO. We owe special gratitude to two former students: Brittany Ammerman for the funding, implementation and sustainability of the Nikumbuke Soccer League, and to Aubrey Winkie for bringing to life the Moringa Tree Sustainability and Co-operative Project. Rebecca Mandich also deserves deep words of appreciation for recovering oral histories of women, transcribe them and translate them Kiswahili-English. Those stories, along with many health related educational materials were published through the first African *Cartonera Kutsemba Cartão* (Cardboard Hope) created in Maputo-Mozambique by Saylín Alvarez and Louis Madureira. Saylín and Louis published dozens of HbM cardboard books that have preserved oral stories, health related *dramas,* and learning/teaching tools for health promotion and disease prevention that otherwise would have been lost; these books were widely available in the villages of Kwale County and are also kept in a special collection at the University of Wisconsin-Madison Memorial Library. Former graduate students Erin Campeau and Michele Coleman also merit heartfelt words of recognition for their work: Erin brought to life the Moringa Tree Training in the seven communities, and Michele conducted a very thoughtful and academically acclaimed fieldwork on reproductive health among the women. Finally, thank you to graduate student, Kate Austin, who wrote the first capstone paper and diagram on the Health by All Means model.

We are also very grateful to FOTA (From One To Another), the Swedish organization who has graciously assisted Nikumbuke-Health by Motorbike since 2012 with various types of funding. FOTA has recently created a system of scholarships for the secondary education of "Nikumbuke girls" and has achieved great success in keeping girls in school and in motivating them for higher education.

The projects addressed in this book would have not been possible without the generous support of the Rotary Madison West, the UW-Madison Morgridge Center for Public Service, the Ira and Ineva Reilly Baldwin Wisconsin Idea Endowment, and the Davis Foundation for Projects for Peace. The financial support of friends and family members cannot be underestimated either since it has been of crucial importance for the implementation and sustainability of many of the health projects and for moving them forward.

Film documentarists Reynaldo Morales, Liliane Calfee and James Choi directed and produced two of the documentaries that made visible the work of the women and helped us attract funders and potential support. Thanks to the Wisconsin State Journal, USA Today Newspaper, and BRAVA magazine for their in-depth reporting of the projects in the villages. Deepest gratitude goes to Wisconsin Channel 27 (*WKOW 27*), especially to Anchor Amber Noggle for her thoughtful coverage of the work of our UW-Madison team in Kwale County.

We are indebted to Dr. Federico Mayor Zaragoza and his Foundation Culture of Peace, for the nomination of Nikumbuke Health by Motorbike to the United Nations Public Service Award in 2013. We are honored to have Dr. Mayor Zaragoza's preliminary words for this book; he is a moral inspiration for us. We are also very grateful to Dr. Margarita Benítez for her poignant comments and meticulous reading of the final manuscript. Very special thanks go to Cristina González and Pu Chia, graduate students from Autonomous University of Madrid, for their valuable contribution in the revisions of the manuscript and the elaboration of the Infogram. Their contributions were carried out as part of a practicum for the Interdisciplinary Gender Studies Master program of Autonomous University of Madrid at the Foundation Culture of Peace-Women's Knowledge International. In this context, our gratitude also goes to Irene Antón Pintado and Maysa Hajjaj for her assistance in the preparation of grant proposals.

We cannot finish our words of gratitude without acknowledging the unfailing support of Harvard Professor Doris Sommer; her trust, her optimism and her belief in human creativity to subvert structural violence have been pivotal. Besides, it was precisely Dr. Sommer who named this health promotion and wellbeing movement "Health by All Means;" we deeply thank her!

## COMMENTS

The quest for gender equity and the eradication of violence against women is pervasive and a significant aspect of cultures around the globe. To be sure, indigenous feminisms exist in most patriarchal contexts, even, presumably, in the least likely places. HEALTH BY ALL MEANS: WOMEN TURNING STRUCTURAL VIOLENCE INTO HEALTH AND WELLBEING is a remarkable and rare case study of the possibility of an egalitarian, respectful partnership between a U.S. university and rural villages in Kenya as they engage in a variety of women's empowerment strategies that are sustainable over time. The book is a riveting exploration of the joys of "feminist emotion" as a tool for radical social change.

**Beverly Guy-Sheftall**
Anna Julia Cooper Professor of Comparative
Women's Studies at Spelman College and co-editor
of *Words of fire: an anthology of African American feminist thought.*

With the charm and wisdom that confirms her deep humanity on every page, Araceli Alonso offers a model for interventions in apparently intractable situations. This is no recipe book for promoting health, because "all means" include careful and customized attention to available resources and strategies. But Alonso is an inspiration to follow, a spirit who explores and collaborates, counting on women to muster enough urgency and good humor to tackle patriarchy, poverty, and ethnic tensions in rural Kenya, and far beyond.

**Doris Sommer**
Director of Cultural Agents Initiative at
Harvard University, Ira and Jewell Williams Jr.
Professor of Romance Languages and Literatures
and of African and African American Studies.

The stories and achievements from this book have inspired the trajectory of my own future. The efforts by the women of Lunga Lunga and Kwale county have created a sustainable way of making a holistically healthy life more accessible for all, while tightening community bonds and providing them with a strong sense of meaning and capability. The book details an incredible example of the power of indigenous knowledge, and the importance of humility when working cross culturally. The Health by All Means work serves as an invaluable example to forming a sustainable bridge to the brightest attainable future for oppressed women. The powerful lessons in this book are essential to all areas of life and conflict that we deal with today. This is something that all people aiming to work in global health need to read!

**Grant M Klausen**
Former Director, University of Oregon
Students for Global Health.

This compelling book combines feminist theoretical rigor with applied research, a heartwarming story of multicultural understanding and collaboration, and astute pointers for effective community action at home and abroad.

**Margarita Benitez**
Executive Director
Puerto Rico Endowment for the Humanities.

As students and young professionals in a world so obfuscated and mired by short-sighted and poorly executed global health interventions, it has become increasingly difficult to determine the appropriate way to live and work in this climate. Dr. Alonso's work serves as a beacon, cutting through the fog of uncertainty, and establishes a stellar framework for how to go about enacting meaningful change. Her Health by All Means model for development and wellbeing establishes a new and revolutionary standard for the empowerment and betterment of men and women alike. Dr. Alonso's model goes above and beyond others by realizing that healthcare is only one component of success, and shows how working with the community to empower, enable, and educate women is crucial to the wellbeing of all. As the next generation of global citizens, Dr. Alonso gives us the tools to fight the helplessness and apathy that so often stops people from getting the help they deserve in a mindful and lasting way, and I strongly recommend this book to any student who seeks concrete examples of how to apply the knowledge we've gained from education.

**Andrew Pardi**
MD student, Former Executive director
University of Oregon Students for Global Health

# FOREWORD

The most relevant journey is captured within the pages of this book, co-written by Araceli Alonso and Teresa Langle de Paz, two figures of extraordinary human value. The authors offer the reader something to hold on to and reflect upon for the new steps of this era that is just beginning. Teresa Langle de Paz incessantly and courageously pursues spaces of knowledge, intellectual keys and models of wisdom for the equal dignity of all human beings. She intelligently reflects upon what she sees and observes. Araceli Alonso tells us about the marvelous grassroots work that she has promoted and that—no wonder—received the highest recognition on public service from the United Nations.

Araceli Alonso and Teresa Langle de Paz take a high fly in this book and propose us venues to transform structural violence into peace and wellbeing. Such great transition from power force to the power of words, from a culture of violence and subjection to a culture of alliance, convergence and conciliation is the very precious fruit that is often collected after tenaciously harvesting in stony and inhospitable soil. From violence to harmony and peaceful coexistence; the secret is that both, Araceli and Teresa, walk around the world, as the Spanish poet Miguel Hernández recommended: "carrying love on their shoulders".

**Federico Mayor Zaragoza**
President of the Foundation Culture of Peace,
Former UNESCO Director General.
November 19, 2018.

## INTRODUCTION

Health by All Means documents the transformation of a community with, for, and by women who experience gender-based structural violence. It can be experienced as a story, a philosophy lesson, a walk with a treasured friend, and, at times, a song, and much dancing. It is deeply imbued with the spirit of Araceli Alonso, a University of Wisconsin-Madison teacher, scholar and activist, and the story of her health by motorbike program in rural Kenya. And yet it is so much more than a personal story. The intimate recounting of this development effort becomes universal precisely through the particulars. These details elucidate or common humanity and show us friendship. They tell us why—the reasons we never would guess from disciplinary frameworks or empirical observation. These truths emerge in relationships, and they spark creativity, solidarity and change.

The program was initiated in the context of a university partnership by a faculty member and students at the University of Wisconsin-Madison—including the Department of Gender and Women's Studies, the Global Health Institute and the 4W Women and Wellbeing Initiative. HbAM's success can be attributed to a broad network of actors—including community leaders, students who rotated through and were transformed by it, financial supporters, both individuals and organizations, and from support and recognition by UNESCO.

Here, The *Nikumbuke* Health by All Means story is told in two parts. In Part I Araceli Alonso tells the story of women, often in their own words, from seven villages of the Kwale County, the most southeastern county in the Coast Province of Kenya that borders with Tanzania (Lunga Lunga, Godo, Perani, Umoja, Maasailand, Mpakani and Jirani) as they searched for gender equality, equity, empowerment, and sustainable development on their own terms. The reader truly feels that they are walking with the women as access to water and health care are improved, and women grow in all kinds of ways – from sewing, to planting trees, to dancing, to playing soccer, to knowing that they have a voice. To using that voice.

In Part II, feminist scholar Teresa Langle de Paz, accompanies Ara on her journey with the lens of a philosopher and theoretician. She helps the reader to explore affect, meaning, knowledge construction, and the nature of joy. Her reflections and observations related to the tangible project impacts, and the remarkable social and emotional dynamics engendered, recognize both as essentially embedded in time and place and culture, and at the same time universal.

This book can be used as a guide for collaboration with communities by individuals who would like to engage in local change (Part I) and as a tool for reflection and self-critique before, during or after that process (Part II). These materials can be used in an iterative way, so that readers receive the benefits of seeing and reseing, thinking and rethinking, and finding the kinds of fresh and deep insights that are only discovered through reflection, analysis and revision of the stories and examples.

The HbAM model presented at the end of part I can be useful to individuals and organizations that hope to develop similar long-term transformative community-led partnerships.

The work of N-HbM draws on the assets of many disciplines, but most importantly, as Alonso states, it takes advantage of the "interpellations and contestations of multiple disciplines— public health, gender studies and feminisms, medical anthropology, history, philosophy, and peace studies among others; because no one single discipline, or even the combination of them, can tell the whole story." This interdisciplinary approach has allowed us to challenge different disciplines, and center the lives of women, in their work towards gender equality, sustainable health and women's wellbeing.

The world is full of structural violence, and it is full of possibilities. These two narratives about the Health by All Means project in Kenya, reveal two different and complementary lessons. First, Araceli Alonso shows us that change must happen in the particular, and it must be created with and for communities. It must be based on their lived experiences and articulated in their own voice, through their own culture, and with their unique creativity. We are left wondering then, how long it will take to move from transforming a village to creating a culture of peace in the world. Teresa Langle de Paz, in her theoretical analysis which portrays this change process as an example of feminist emotion at work, gives us reason to hope that indeed this change process can and is likely to emerge in many places, and gives us reason to expect that it will flower in many different ways.

Taken together, the work of Alonso and Langle de Paz suggests that the transformation of structural violence to wellbeing and a culture of peace is not only possible, but likely, and perhaps, inevitable.

**Lori Diprete Brown**
Associate Director of the Global Health Institute and Director of the 4W Initiative at the University of Wisconsin-Madison

## FIRST CONNECTIONS

### Araceli: My First Connection

In 2007 I sent a letter to a P.O. Box to a woman named Mariamu in a place whose name I could not even pronounce well, "Lunga-Lunga." I thought I was writing letters to a person I would never meet, and that person in turn would write back to me from her very distant part of the world. The alleged purpose was improvement of skills in written English for women in rural parts of Kenya.

Our first letters were brief, using words like tiny brushstrokes to construct simple portraits of our worlds. With time, our letters invited us to assemble words and complete sentences and consider word choices to describe ourselves and those around us. Although distance prevented us from meeting in person, the letters helped us to connect, develop a friendship, open up a dialogue and create a mindful and meaningful way to relate among, through and between us. The two of us, our families, and our communities became connected with every letter. My daughter Sofia, then 14, became pen-pals with her 16-year old daughter Peninah, who was pregnant at the time expecting her first child.

Through our epistolary relationship, my *rafiki*[1] Mariamu and I discovered that we had many more similarities than differences. We were from far away countries, spoke different languages, had different ways to understand religion, different skin tones, different clothing, that is: we had different labels that belonged to different categories, but our humanity was strikingly

---

[1] *Rafiki* means friend and friendship in Kiswahili, and that is the way we referred to each other since then: "My *rafiki*".

similar. We shared feelings we both felt, wantings we both wanted, desires we both desired; we were very much alike regardless the undemocratic way of being born under unequal circumstances. One of the most important aspects of our pen-pal conversations, however, was the feeling of knowing that we were somewhere there for each other, to read each other: "I am here, I care about you, I think of you often and I put my soul in your hands with every word I write."

Two years into our letter writing, I had the opportunity to do research in east Africa (Kampala, Uganda), and decided to try to find my *rafiki* at last.

After four exhausting and interminable days traveling by bus, train, car, *tuk-tuk*, ferry, *matatu*, and *boda-boda*,[2] I finally reached Godo, a village of scattered houses in the savannah located at the east border of Kenya and Tanzania. In my pocket, I had the first letter that Mariamu had written to me two years back. I did not know, but Mariamu was waiting for me with the first letter I had written to her, in her hands. Along with Mariamu there were around 50 other women from the village of Godo, all waiting for me, inside a dark room of a tiny building made of mud and grass. Coming in the room from the bright midday Kenyan sun, I could not see a soul, but soon I witnessed what I thought were hundreds of smiles and expectant eyes. We emotionally greeted each other, I read Mariamu's letter and she read mine. The women saw that Mariamu and I had created a strong link through our passionate correspondence. Letters had brought us together through time and space, escaping whatever facts and life circumstances separated us. And now I was there.

---

[2] *Tuk-tuk* refers to a three-wheeled cabin cycle very popular in Mombasa to get around the city. *Boda-boda* are motorcycle taxis commonly found in east Africa. *Matatu* are privately owned minibuses that work as shared large taxis. Many *matatu* are colorfully decorated featuring famous people with enticing slogans. *Matatu* often play loud music to quickly attract riders who are waiting or passing by the roads

## Teresa: My First Connection

In 2011, I had the chance to fortuitously meet Araceli Alonso at a reception of the Gender and Women's Studies Department at the University of Wisconsin, Madison in the United States. I happened to be at Madison, visiting from Spain for a conference where I was going to present an initiative that I had just co-founded: Women's Knowledge International. The more I got to know N-HbM's work in Kenya, the stronger my admiration grew. The dedicated spirit, intuitive vision, professionalism, scientific rigor, and most of all, the qualities as a human being of Araceli Alonso were, no doubt, related to the success of the programs. But even if my first appreciation of the programs might have been subjectively tainted by an incipient friendship, it was also scientifically informed by my own expertise on feminist theory and gender issues. It was clear to me that I was encountering something extremely relevant for certain feminist agendas, and that it needed to be examined theoretically. My task then came about as something unavoidable: some core principles, premises and components of a gender, health and development model that seemed rather unique, needed to be extrapolated.

The world is full of very capable and amazing people—I thought—who could make a real difference for women and communities who may desperately need help. But as I learned details about the Nikumbuke programs in Lunga Lunga as well as nearby villages, and reflected upon them, I realized that the capable people that I was thinking about were not outsiders to the local communities, but the very same women who "desperately needed" something to take place in their lives and communities for their daily wellbeing to improve. This was a very relevant realization because, in fact, it pointed at the first sign of distinctiveness to the replicable model that this book is about:

The local women collectively decide what they want for their lives and what needs to be done, and have a sense of complete ownership towards the programs.[3]

Although I had read much criticism on participative and democratic pedagogies and methodologies, I was still a bit puzzled by this initial realization. The strategies and methods used to address health matters comprehensively as wellbeing by the local NGO—N-HbM—and by Araceli Alonso as director and supervisor from the University of Wisconsin-Madison seemed to go one step further from similar initiatives that I had knowledge of (Denzin and Giardina 2010). What was taking place in Lunga Lunga was "different." Yes. But what was so special about it?

I began by asking many operational questions to myself and to Araceli Alonso. I came up with basic initial inquiries related to her role as the main international facilitator and that of the university students who assisted her in the implementation of the grass-roots programs each summer. My inquiries also spun around the mechanics of the work that had been going on in Lunga Lunga. For instance, I wondered about the tasks of the local coordinator, a Kenyan woman named Bendettah Thomas, and the means through which she had become the overall program supervisor; and what was the kind of support Alonso relied on from the American university where she was a professor. I also wondered if there were any previous research, assessment, direct knowledge and contact with the communities, structuring and planning undertaken before the women from the villages of Lunga Lunga began doing their own work; and so on.

---

[3] Underscored sections are meant to guide readers in the gathering process of some of the key ideas of my analysis and the components of the programs.

The on-site achievements over the years seemed to have been rather effortless and to be flowing "on their own." It seemed communities were very successfully navigating through complicated obstacles related to customary gender norms, ethnically based prejudices, tribal clashes, culturally rooted habits, religious differences; in addition, there were very harsh living circumstances including endemic disease, poor nutrition, lack of electricity and clean water, scarcity of basic medical assistance, isolation, or limited access to education. But such characteristics were no different from the means through which so many other successful development initiatives operated around the world.

I came to conclude that the real challenge was to delve into other than tangible or mechanic grounds for N-HbM effectiveness; further, the goal should be to theoretically explain how and why the scope of its impact was larger and deeper than its visible and mechanical aspects. The purpose of my research was to further intellectually explore the fascinating paradox of the fact that the appearance of simplicity concealed a harmonious entangled complexity, regardless of how and when such complex program structuring was articulated. Carefully planned micro steps informed by scientific rigor and respect for people's dignity in diversity seemed to have created such a beautiful and empowering network. Little did I know, until much later, that I had already come down with one of the keys to N-HbM success:

> A "simple-common-sense" approach to human communication, connection, and capacity-building anchored by scholarly rigor.

But the questions that kept running through my mind made this reasoning more and more unsatisfactory and insufficient as an explanation. The task in front of me was of a unique nature: the hardest but perhaps most important aspects to N-HbM programs were the elusive forces that seemed to lurk there, not its functioning mechanisms and specific components and programs *per se*. I wanted to go to Lunga Lunga, and the nearby villages, to see it for myself.

# PART I

# ETHNOGRAPHY

## Araceli Alonso

## Background


This first part of the book tells the story of women, often in their own words, from seven villages of the Kwale County, the most southeastern county in the Coast Province of Kenya that borders with Tanzania—Lunga Lunga, Godo, Perani, Umoja, Maasailand, Mpakani and Jirani—, as they searched for gender equality, equity, empowerment, and sustainable development in their own terms.

Lunga Lunga is a border town, located within walking distance of the Horohoro border crossing into Tanzania (Figure 1). In 2009 Lunga Lunga had a population of 15,276 of which 10,015 were estimated to be living in poverty, defined as a monthly adult income of Ksh 2,913 or less (approximately $30 USD) (MLDPP 2011, 47; KNBS 2010; KNBS 2013, 6). Lunga Lunga is a small, two-road town, yet it is the only of the seven locations that can be located on a map; the other villages are simply too small and remote. Lunga Lunga is similar to many other border towns: it hosts a small but bustling market, a transit hotel, and its single paved road sees a near constant stream of trucks coming to and from Tanzania. With Ukunda and Mombasa within a few hours' drive, the crossing is strategically important for both the Kenyan and Tanzanian governments.

The Kenyan Coast Province in general has struggled with poverty-related health concerns and higher-than-average rates of child mortality when compared to the national average (MLDPP 2011, 49). Malaria in particular has been ranked the number one cause of death and morbidity in Kwale County, followed by respiratory diseases, skin diseases, and diarrhea (MLDPP 2011, 41). There is a single county hospital that is inaccessible to many residents who cannot afford transportation costs. This hospital, located 75 kilometers from Lunga Lunga, lacks a theater and x-ray department and is surrounded by poor road networks (MLDPP

2011, 128). Thirty nine percent of the county residents (and 45% of the Lunga Lunga population) have no formal education and only 10% of the county population has a secondary education level or above (KNBS, 2013, 12).

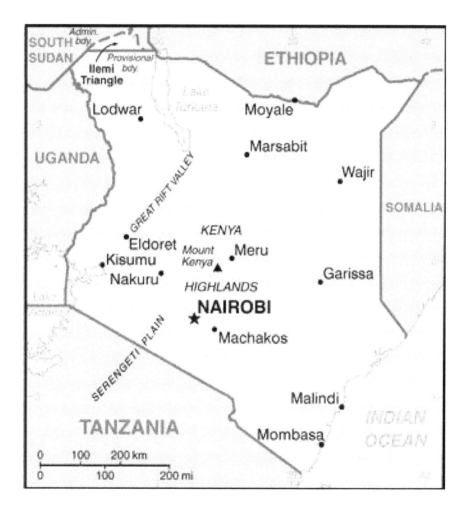

**Figure 1.** Map of Kenya. Kwale County is located south of Mombasa; the seven villages mentioned in this book border the east southern coast, between Kenya and Tanzania (CIA, The World Factbook, January 2019, Public domain, https://www.cia.gov/library/publications/the-world-fact book/geos/ke.html).

In terms of environmental quality, the Kwale County's ecosystem has been quickly declining. Kwale County's land is semi-arid, receiving between 500 and 1,200mm of rainfall per year and facing challenges associated with semi-desert areas—reduced access to safe drinking water and decreased crop production due to poor soil quality (MLDPP 2011, 20;UNDP 2013, 8-9). Average rainfall decreases with distance inland, putting Lunga Lunga at a geographical disadvantage. The current forest cover is a mere 7%, and with a 0.25% per annum deforestation rate—a loss of 19,580 hectares every 10 years, Kwale County's forest cover is expected to be almost non-existent by 2034 (MLDPP 2011, 30-31). As a result, food is likely to become scarcer, as already infertile soil becomes even less able to produce crops (MLDPP 2011, 24).

The social composition in Kwale County is a reflection of the diversity of the country in which it is located. Kwale County is populated by two main ethnic groups: the Digo (60%) and the Duruma (25%) (MLDPP 2011, 53). Other ethnic groups include Kamba, Luo, Taita, Luhya, Giriama, Kisee, Makondo, Shirazi, and Maasai. Each tribe has its own unique customs, traditions, and history, as well as history of relations and interactions with other tribes in the area. Survey data also demonstrates the role of religion in this area, with 43.9 per cent of the population identifying as Christian, 50.6 per cent identifying as Muslim, and 0.1 per cent identifying as "other" (MLDPP 2011, 59). Family organization centers on male clan leaders and respected village male elders who are tasked with making important community decisions (MLDPP 2011, 59).

## The Situation upon Arrival

When I arrived to finally meet Mariamu, staying with the women more than a few days was not in my plans. Life in Lunga Lunga and in Godo seemed too hard: no running water, no available toilets, no electricity, and walking through the savannah from house to house was tough enough for me as I was developing post-polio syndrome.

The women, however, started sharing their stories with me, their homes, their meals, their concerns, their laughter, their everything with me! How could I not stay? How could I stay? As a nurse I wanted to stay, as a medical anthropologist I wanted to stay, as a human being I wanted to stay, but my urban upbringing was still shouting otherwise. It was the questions of the Mamas[4] and their insistence in learning the answers what would determine my longer stay: "Why does my back hurt?" "Why do I have heartburn?" Why do I have vaginal discharge?"

I managed to answer those questions, but I personally needed to understand.

I sought the help of the Head of the Lunga Lunga Health Center, a government facility run by a Head Nurse, known as Dr. Mwangi[5], who helped me conduct a simple health base assessment as per request of the women. Very soon, we detected a number of directly and indirectly health related issues: 1) Low life expectancy by Western standards—many people did not live longer than forty years—, quite shocking at first sight. 2) Child marriage of girls and adolescents was quite common, a fact that implied a number of health related matters, such as early pregnancy, high maternal and infant mortality rates, vesico-vaginal fistula, severe anemia,

---

[4] The term *Mama* refers to women in general as "Lady" or "Mrs." but it is also used interchangeable with the term "Mother." Often the terms *Mama* and *Madam* are used interchangeably to refer to a lady in the community adding her first name. In that way, this manuscript uses Mama and Madam interchangeably.

[5] I am purposely keeping the title of "Dr." for Mr. Mwangi although he is not a medical doctor but a Head Nurse Practitioner. There are very few MDs in rural Kenya and none at all in this area. Mr. Mwangi is known in the villages as "Doctor Mwangi" and that is a deference I want to keep for him; his vast knowledge, his expertise and good will, and his inner kindness with all patients make him well deserved of this honorific title.

miscarriage, stillborn babies, premature and low weight babies; higher exposure to diseases (malaria and HIV). 3) Female Genital *Circumcision*[6] was very extended among some ethnic groups, with severe risk of hemorrhage, sepsis, tetanus, trauma of adjacent structures, urinary tract infection, HIV. 4) Myths, legends and culturally-based beliefs may have had dangerous consequences for health; for instance, the belief on a disease caused by bad spirits or *degedege*, which could only be treated by a traditional healer, and stopped people from receiving medical treatment for other illnesses on time. 5) The lack of basic resources like medicines, drinking water and latrines, clearly had a negative impact on people's health. 6) Lack of public services, or services that were out of reach for the majority of the population, especially the rural population, made access to health services and hospitals very difficult for patients or for health professionals; sometimes there was no means of transportation at all and the roads were very difficult to transit.

A Global Health expert would have immediately deduced that there were two major problems to address: on the one hand, infectious diseases that spread rapidly in the community and on the other hand, common illnesses that could be easily prevented became endemic. The question was: How to address these problems so that positive change would last and be sustainable?

---

[6] We have written the term as the women in the villages refer to it "circumcision." The World Health Organization, however, refers to the practice as "mutilation" (FGM) and defines it as all procedures that involve partial or total removal of the external female genitalia, or other injury to the female genital organs for non-medical reasons http://www.who.int/mediacentre/factsheets/fs241/en/. Some of the tribes in Kwale County have abandoned the practice, others perform Type 1 Clitoridectomy—partial or total removal of the clitoris, and Type 2 Excision—partial or total removal of the clitoris and the labia minora with or without excision of the labia majora.

## Plans in Action

To many, gender equality and the empowerment of women might seem too massive to even start thinking towards the achievement of a minimum goal. If we add to those aspirations the procurement of women's health and wellbeing, and sustainable development and peace building, our overwhelming uncertainty would have discouraged us while the mistakes and the damages of the past inflicted in the name of progress and development would have prevented us completely from moving forward. Apparently, the challenges are too vast and our fears too many, so there is a tendency to predict that our work towards the achievement of those goals would bring nothing positive at all. As a result, our apprehension and fearfulness put the mechanism of the Prophecy of Nothing in action: if "nothing" is the ineludible outcome of our work towards a better and fairer world, we will do nothing to remediate the establishment and change the status quo, therefore there will be no change, nothing will happen and consequently the predicted Prophecy of Nothing will, once again, be indisputably fulfilled.

In order to counteract the Prophecy of Nothing, the programs of HbAM[7] (Health by All Means) and of N-HbM (Nikumbuke-Health by Motorbike) used a subversive, imperfect, and impertinent imagination informed and nourished by an interdisciplinary body of knowledge, to ignite a transformative movement resulting in women turning structural violence into health, wellbeing, and a culture of peace.

---

[7] Health by All Means (HbAM) serves as an umbrella for smaller efforts adapted to different geographical and cultural circumstances. In the case of Kenya, the movement began as Health by Motorbike (HbM) and was named by the women as Nikumbuke "Remember me" in Kiswahili. After that moment, the movement became well known in Kenya as Nikumbuke-Health by Motorbike (N-HbM).

### Working Towards Empowerment and Unity

From the very beginning, women in the villages who became members of N-HbM had recognized their historically marginal place in their respective communities. As Madam Bendettah[8] mentioned in a personal interview[9]:

"I decided to work with women and girls because I saw that there was a purpose in empowering women. When you go to a community, you find that some years back, women there were really oppressed. So we wanted–or I wanted–to open this one [Nikumbuke-HbM] so that our women and girls... could know their rights."

Nurse Josephine[10] shared similar sentiments:

"Nikumbuke-HbM is important for the women in this community because you find that most of the women... in the families or in the community, most of the women... they are not valued. That's why we find that when we had to start the Nikumbuke Project, it was empowering girls and women. Because most of them... they had no value in their community."

The concept of Health by All Means was conceived within the framework of the small USA/Kenyan organization named Health by Motorbike (HbM) that the local women baptized in Kiswahili as *Nikumbuke*, meaning "remember me." Nikumbuke-

---

[8] Local Director of N-HbM programs. Bendettah Muthina Thomas is referred by the women as Madam Bendettah, Mama Bendettah, or just Madam.
[9] Personal interview conducted by graduate student Erin Campeau for her Master Thesis, August 2014, Lunga Lunga.
[10] Madam Josephine was a fruit seller with some formal knowledge of nursing, although no official title. She became the Nurse of Nikumbuke-HbM because the women trusted her in the first place.

HbM, then, was formed based on the fact that each woman was seeking her own voice. As a group, they understood that their collective echo might more strongly reverberate.

To start illustrating the way in which N-HbM was conceived and implemented for the delivery of its health programs, I have chosen the term *Umoja*, which means "unity" in Kiswahili and that expresses the basic characteristics of unity and solidarity needed to successfully achieve any kind of human relationships. But unity and solidarity, not because women are good, have good feelings and sentiments, or because they are all very religious or very humanitarian. Unity and solidarity were understood in this context as intrinsic to human relations and communication, promoting responsibility about what we said and did to ourselves, to others, to the environment.

This *Umoja* approach acknowledged transversal leadership, influencing and motivating without a hierarchy or a formal authority. This approach also recognized women as valid interlocutors in a community, recovering the 19th century Latin etymological meaning of *persons,* women as *persons,* "*per*" as a prefix of intensification plus the verb "*sonare*" to make a sound, to sound through[11]. This notion validated each woman as a person: "I am a person and I am here!" "I can hear but I can also be heard!" "I speak and also amplify my voice!" This position led to the self-analysis and self-reflection of all the participants involved—those who prepared the programs and those who received them, with unity, solidarity and empathy.

The *Umoja* approach made us even question the personal pronouns "they" and "we" over and over again, alternating the terms and changing them back and forth. Although the women

---

[11] The etymological meaning of *person* has been long debated. This narrative uses the meaning of the Oxford Etymology Dictionary https://www.etymonline.com/word/person, also used by Spanish peace philosopher Vicent García Guzmán (2005).

from the seven villages have carried out and owned the N-HbM projects, the *Umoja* approach tried to avoid the use of "they" [the women] since it distanced and detached them from "us" giving us all a false and impossible sense of separation. This approach, however, does not imply that "we" women are a homogenous collective unit and therefore have the same needs. Women are a heterogeneous group; their lives and needs vary depending on socio-economic status, racial/ethnic background, sexual orientation, region and sub-region, national origin, religion, citizenship, health, and disability, among other variables.

## Health Promotion and Health Education

Although from my first arrival in Lunga Lunga, I did not introduce myself as a university professor, I could not ignore the fact that as the women started knowing more about me, they perceived my knowledge to be "authoritative" in the sense that I had had the privilege to learn in a university setting. Similarly, I trained my students to think this way–with humility and generosity about their knowledge. My aim in the process of health promotion was not to be seen as an authority figure or to give an "authoritative knowledge" by any means, but to be a mediator of resources and a learning facilitator, a conductor of a symphony carefully conceived by the women and harmoniously performed also by the women. My goal was for the women to acquire what they wanted to acquire so desperately—a knowledge that was deprived from them and that could give them the opportunity to develop more confidence in themselves and exert self-reliance and independence.

### Women's Summer Health Camps

N-HbM has followed the assumption that health education can have either beneficial or harmful effects on people's lives and wellbeing. In Lunga Lunga, the women requested a basic health education program, not because they thought they needed it but because they knew they wanted it. In 2010, three undergraduate students from UW-Madison, my own 16-year old daughter and myself decided to deliver what the women wanted. From March to June, we prepared the curriculum according to the wishes of the women: maternal health, infectious diseases, sexual transmitted infections, malaria prevention, basic nutrition and hygiene. Thanks to a grant from the Davis Foundation for Projects for Peace, we were able to organize summer health camps for approximately 300 women—around 100 women from each of the three villages of Lunga Lunga, Godo and Perani.

The structure of the health camps was informal and decentralized, leaving the organization, planning and decision making into the hands of the community leaders who in turn were informed by the wishes of the women. The health camp in each village lasted one week and the training started at 8:00am and ended at 4:30pm. We had two short breaks to stretch and a longer lunch break when all of us ate together, interacted, chatted, danced, sang and shared laughter. Meals and beverages for all were provided by the grant, and at the end of the health camp the women received an in-kind compensation for their attendance to the training. The first intention of the UW-Madison teaching team was to incentivize the women with a small amount of money to compensate the time they were not working in their *chambas*[12]. The women, however, requested no money and instead suggested beans, rice and sugar because "Our husbands can take that money if they wish but with the food the whole family eats."

---

[12] Plot of land for harvesting.

A pivotal moment that considerably determined the forth-coming relationship between the N-HbM team and the women came at lunch in each of the three villages where the camps were held. When the camps started, we were considered visitors, "guests," and as such we were going to be treated. For the first lunch, the women served us first, and as we would discover later the meal was substantially different for us, more nutritious, which immediately made us think that the women knew well what a balanced meal, unaffordable for them, entailed. As our meals were covered by the grant, the women probably thought we deserved a more privileged treatment. While the women only ate rice and beans, our "guests" meal consisted of rice and beans but also served with meat, vegetables and fruits. It was not our intention to be disrespectful or ungrateful, on the contrary we were very moved by the generosity and hospitality of the women. However, we felt that breaking bread with the women and eating the same meal, whatever that meal was, would be the ethical thing to do; also, a way to create a common space and a move towards community building. Certainly, even after the first meal together we witnessed a transformation in the attitudes and openness of all of us. It seemed like the act of intentionally eating together had shuttered barriers and transformed that lunch moment into something unique and meaningful, giving us a sense of togetherness and even opening up a space for celebration. While during lesson time, the N-HbM team was in charge of facilitating the learning process, which inevitably separated us between "instructors" and "students," lunch time would be a way for all of us to nourish our bodies and our relationship, with no power structure and in a deeper level. We were not instructors or students, we were not colleagues; we were friends. At that moment, we noticed that the dynamic changed, paving the way for collaboration, friendship, and quality work.

During the health camps, women voiced their own ideas, suggestions, questions, and figured out solutions by themselves and for themselves assisted by the UW-Madison team that facilitated and moderated the discussion. A decisive moment in Godo was when Mama Veronica asked out loud:

"When should we cut the umbilical cord of a baby?"

Then a discussion began about giving birth at home or in the clinic: "I assisted the birth of my own twins, but one of them died days later, his neck stiff and his body bended like this [showing backwards]," Mama Veronica intervened again. Some women knew right away, "Tetanus!" shouted two of them. Mama Esther added that the traditional way to cut the umbilical cord with the thumbnail could sometimes be a contributor of disease if the hands were not cleaned enough. Another Mama commented that not only the umbilical cord was cut with the thumbnail but also sometimes the perineum, "that's why some women around here keep their fingernail long and strong like a knife." Nonetheless, the women were not blaming anybody for bad habits or behavior; through their discussion they realized that the lack of tools and the lack of water were two of the main causes of using fingernails to cut the umbilical cord.

"We can't use a knife to cut because we had no clean water to prepare the knife," the women went further.

"But Mama Veronica's baby died because he was not vaccinated at birth" Mama Margret commented.

"Why wasn't he vaccinated," I asked, consciously trying to elicit our own learning.

"Because she didn't know that a vaccine could be used," said one.

"Because she didn't know that the vaccine was her right," said another.

"Because she had no transportation to take the baby to the clinic" said another one.

"Because the clinic was too far away" added another Mama.

"Because rural women are very neglected. We can't go to the clinic if is that far, so the clinic should be closer to our homes," protested Mama Leah from Mpakani, "We are very isolated!" she insisted.

The main goal of these health summer camps was not to change women's "bad" habits or behaviors but rather to facilitate their own learning process by which they could understand by themselves the many variables and circumstances that could cause poor health and how to tackle those variables in order to promote wellbeing. We did not question women's values, believes or habits since that would have meant to put into question women's own identities and to challenge the way they define themselves within their groups. However, the women themselves brought up traditions, values and beliefs that they wanted to discuss in an open and welcoming environment. It was often the women the ones who challenged traditions and listened to the points of view of women from other ethnic groups; they were not seeking answers but rather a valid interlocutor that would listen without judging.

The circumstances of Mama Veronica's baby gave us a chance to start a discussion that went beyond life and death, beyond health and disease; it took us to a place in which women discovered by themselves what was needed, at individual and structural levels, in case another Mama had to go through the same situation. It seemed that the women were able to link health with other aspects of social development. We all together explored the causes of poverty and poor health, as they are closely associated. Mama Bendettah orchestrated the effort: each household with women in reproductive years would be required to have a *kiberiti kit* containing the most basic utensils to cut the umbilical cord—a tiny container of the size of a matchbox with a pair of gloves, a new razor blade, and a thread to tie the cord; "And a clean kanga[13] to wrap the baby!" another Mama added. However, the women went further realizing that cutting the cord was not the only lethal decision they had encountered, "My neighbor died bleeding after she delivered her baby; no one could save her" one Mama said. "That happened to my neighbor too!" added one, "Mine too!" added another one, and the voices of other women resonated like an endless echo in the room "Mine too, mine too, too, too...!" The women talked about bleeding, about the placenta not coming out entirely, about fever and convulsions, about spirits that come from the water and make women sick, about the snake that often comes to kill the mother and steal the baby.

The women one by one and all together deciphered the "Three Delay Model" that we often use in our university courses to explain maternal mortality around the world: "My mother-in-law said that women are cowards if they go to the clinic to have babies," said one of the young Mamas. The other women giggled looking at each other, recognizing themselves in the comment, some as mothers-in-law and some as daughters-in-law. The debate began. Some mentioned that husbands were mostly absent when babies were born and that their mothers-in-law were very insensitive to their pains of labor and that some lives could have been saved if the mothers-in-law would have helped in the first place. For the first time women in the villages were talking together about issues that had never been discussed before. Although at first mothers-in-law protested, they soon realized that they were also daughters-in-law themselves and that the claim sounded way too familiar for them too. The women, young and old, made a pledge to overcome some of the difficulties that pregnant women confronted in their communities, starting at home. The women themselves had deciphered the First Delay: recognizing the potential problem at home.

---

[13] Traditional piece of fabric used as a skirt, shawl, or even towel or blanket.

The second delay was easy for the women to talk about without anybody else mentioning at all:

"But, what do I do?" protested one Mama. "I pretend I don't care because what else can I do if I see my daughter-in-law struggling and my son is not home?"

"Call the healer!" answered one with a mischievous tone while the others laughed hard.

"You have to take her to the clinic!" said one.

"How?" kept protesting the first Mama.

Silence... The women had decoded the Second Delay: getting from home to the clinic; transportation!

"But sometimes the clinic can't help either. My sister had to be taken to the hospital after she reached the clinic; the clinic couldn't help her. She lost a lot of blood in the way, but the hospital had no blood. We had no money to go there and give our blood for her. My sister and her family had no money to pay the hospital either."

The Third Delay decoded: difficulty at the clinic and hospital levels.

The women discussed the Three Delays, acknowledging that the forms of the delays may vary according to different circumstances. Some of the women were able to look far beyond the immediate causes of maternal complications and showed very critical attitudes towards the third delay, saying that sometimes the hospital is closed for admissions when the Mama arrives, or that the doctors are not available, or that women are often mistreated or treated like children to be scolded. Without knowing it, the women were talking about obstetric violence.[14] The women were clear, the fear of mistreatment in hospitals keeps women

[14] Term coined in the United States to refer to the inhumane treatment of women in labor and delivery wards during childbirth.

preferring to deliver at home assisted by a neighbor or by themselves.

There they were, women from at least nine different ethnic groups and three different religions[15] discussing issues that cut across ethnicity and religion in a country divided and brutally confronted along tribal animosities. Maternal health was a common thread that interweaved the lives of the women in all the villages; soon, the women would discover many other common threads that would drive them to work together in their desire to overcome structural neglect and violence. Health started to be seen among the women as a state of wholeness and wellbeing; achieving that state of wellbeing would require to work together to meet women's needs in a self-reliant and responsible way.

Because maternal health, as well as the other topics, were requested by the women, sharing information helped increase their ability and confidence to solve their own problems, owning the knowledge that was given to them, and utilizing the information in a way they found it reasonable and useful according to their circumstances and specific needs.

For example, the idea of obtaining the *kiberiti kit* was adopted as a way to prevent another case as Mama Veronica's, but the women also decided to create a Mary-Go-Round that would help women in need of some extra money for emergency situations such as the transportation of a pregnant woman to the nearby clinic or hospital. The women also talked about saving for hospital bills. Some of the women decided they would buy a cow as an

---

[15] The ethnic groups presented during the first health training in the villages were Kamba, Duruma, Digo, Giriama, Luhya, Kisee, Makondo, Luo and Taita. In some of the villages the majority of the population is Christian—Lunga Lunga and Godo. In other villages—Perani and Mpakani, approximately half of the population is Muslim and half Christian. Nevertheless, people still believe in spirit possession and still hold traditional values and customs that permeate many levels of their daily lives.

investment, like a savings account, to sell it later in case of need to pay a medical bill.

## Building Creative Community Health and Wellbeing

### *Nikumbuke Health Post*

Although maternal health had provided an important breaking point for our discussions on women's health during the first summer health camps, it was obvious that women regarded health as something more complex than just reproductive health, and that wellbeing went somehow beyond their roles as mothers. The women wanted to understand their bodies, their risks for disease, "Why are we so tired?" "Why my daughter has a discharge?" "Why we have back pains?" "Why I don't see well"? "Why some women are "carriers"[16]? "Why I'm coughing so much"? "What is cancer of the cervix?" The women wanted medical information; getting answers to their questions meant for them to find solutions to their problems.

To give medical advice, or to play doctors and nurses, had never been the intention of N-HbM, and if we wanted to keep working with the women, we would need to clarify the role of N-HbM, our objectives and our goals. In order to answer those questions and help the women to figure out solutions, local nurses and doctors would have to be involved. Two strategies were set in motion: first, Mama Bendettah would search around the communities for a local Mama who had a nursing training and who could commit to work with N-HbM and help the women with their health concerns; second, the government clinic in Lunga Lunga

---

[16] A local way to refer to a person who is HIV +, is "carrier" meaning carrier of the virus.

would need to be involved at all levels of the health training, supervising our work, giving us feedback, and helping the women to figure out the best way to meet their needs. The objective was to plan with the women and not for the women.

In May 2010, nurse Matini became the coordinator of the micro women's health facility opened by N-HbM in Lunga Lunga, named also *Nikumbuke* by the women. While nurse Josephine did not have an official diploma, she had studied two years of nursing in a government facility in Mombasa, and was trusted by the women who sought her services at the local market where Josephine worked as a fruit seller. Dr. Ishmael Mwangi, Head of the Lunga Lunga Health Center, the only government facility in the area, started working with N-HbM also in May 2010. Dr. Mwangi was a crucial piece in the success of N-HbM's health programs since he had already developed a trusting relationship with people in the villages. Dr. Mwangi was an honest, caring and charismatic health professional that introduced us to community health and gave us the chance to start working with a Maasai community.

In July 2010, the *Nikumbuke* Health Post opened to the public under the direction of nurse Josephine and supervised by Dr. Mwangi. The women were again the key actors in the creation of the health facility: baptizing it, choosing the color of the walls and ceiling, picking the furniture and the equipment, and launching it with a big celebration that included women from several neighboring villages. The students and I assisted as needed: for example nurse Josephine selected the color for the walls but requested that the students paint along. We all—the women, the students, and I—participated in the preparation and launching of the health post.

Although opening the health facility was not aimed explicitly at empowering anybody, it did have in fact a positive, even a dramatic impact on our lives. It was evident that the women wanted to be healthy, and wanted to be in control of their bodies and their lives. It was also evident that the students and I wanted to play a part working with the women in advancing their health status. But the opening of the *Nikumbuke* Health Post had consequences that went beyond our imperfect imagination. On the one hand, the facility provided for the women a venue to share their worries and articulate their demands in a private, safe, and discrete manner. The eagerness for this women's health post was undeniable: the same day of the launching, even before the celebration ended, the women made a long line waiting to be seen by nurse Josephine. Issues that had not been discussed before, emerged—infertility, untreated STIs, the desire of controlling fertility, HIV, living with AIDS, undernourishment, domestic violence, unsafe abortion, respiratory problems, untreated skin diseases, lack of energy, work hazards, etc.; issues, conditions and diseases, most of them related to poverty and gender inequities, that many women shared but that had not been openly discussed before. Surprisingly, nurse Josephine became the women's confidante more than the women's nurse. It became noticeable that her lack of skills as a highly trained nurse was not an impediment for her to provide, at very low cost, what the women needed the most: to be listened to, to feel cared for! One year after the opening of the *Nikumbuke* Health Post, nurse Josephine wrote: "I am making good use of the books,[17] I'm very proud of them. I promise this year to change the lives of the women together with their family." Nurse Josephine's health education, a system of referrals with the government health facility, and a door-to-door follow up helped the women to spark a movement that favored health and wellbeing and deliberately avoided illness and disease.

---

[17] Referring to a series of books on women's health by the Hesperian Foundation that we brought a few months earlier—Where Women Have No Doctor, the Book of Midwives http://hesperian.org/books-and-resources/

### *Mama-Toto Mobile Clinic*

For every progress and achievement we made, though, we encountered a challenge and a struggle. "We can't go to Lunga Lunga to see nurse Josephine!" the women from Godo complained. "If we walk three hours to see her, who will fetch water for our homes?" they protested. Indeed, the *Nikumbuke* Health Post was not fairly located to serve women from many communities. The leaders from several villages had spoken, "Lunga Lunga would host the health post." In fact, due to the scattered nature of the settlements in each village, and considering the isolation of many of these communities, the actual location of the health post made sense since Lunga Lunga is closer to a main road and considered a central location in the area. In practical terms, though, the health post would only be viable for women living in Lunga Lunga and from the nearby village of Perani. Women who lived further would need to walk many miles to be seen by nurse Josephine.

Decidedly, if the women could not come to the Health Post, the Health Post would have to go to the women; the idea of the *Mama-Toto* Mobile Clinic emerged! And with it the Health by Motorbike movement took off, originally renting a motorcycle, and soon owning the first motorbike converted into a mobile clinic. The Madison Rotary Club-West provided the first motorbike to carry basic medical equipment—anti-malaria medication, malaria rapid tests, antibiotics, multi-vitamins, anti-parasite tablets, antifungal creams and syrups, first-aid kits, etc. Every Monday afternoon, nurse Josephine would take the *Mama-Toto* to go to Godo, every Tuesday to Jirani, and every Wednesday to Mpakani, Thursday and Friday nurse Josephine would work at the permanent *Nikumbuke* Health Post to serve the women from Perani and Lunga Lunga. Very soon, the *Mama-Toto* would become sustainable: the motorbike was rented out the four days when the mobile clinic did not function; the surplus of Kenyan shillings was good enough to purchase basic medications and save some shillings for gas, future repairs and incidentals. The supply of medications was very limited, but soon it became apparent to nurse Josephine that even more important than medication for the women was the possibility to connect with her, to address their concerns, to talk through things with her, and to feel a sense of inclusion and attachment. Women sometimes needed medications, but they always wanted information. They craved to understand the causes of bad health, the treatment for common illnesses, and even more important, how to prevent disease.

The conviction that the women were creating community grew rapidly around Kwale County; the *"Nikumbuke* women" as they started being known, were working together, planning and carrying out actions for change together. As the news spread, more women wanted to be part of the movement and become "members" of the *Nikumbuke* women. Before long, women from seven villages were participating in the health programs developed by N-HbM, and the *Nikumbuke* Health Post became too small and too crowded to efficiently serve a demanding and deserving population.

In the summer of 2012, when the team of students from UW-Madison was in Lunga Lunga, the decision was made to physically enlarge the health facility. During the year, the students and I had conducted a series of fundraising events in Madison: selling T-shirts, baking muffins, making pancakes, engaging local businesses to "invest in health programs," as we put it, requesting the involvement of other students and faculty, as well as friends and relatives' involvement. In August 2012, with the $7,500 raised and the assistance of FromOne2Another, a newly created not-for-profit organization based in Sweden, the once micro Health Post became the *Nikumbuke* Women's Health Center, with a larger health post, an office for Mama Bendettah to work, a kitchen, a tailoring school, a dentist unit, a library, two latrines, two large outdoor meeting spaces, and three small dwellings for the women to stay as a safe haven and also for future interns to live while staying in Lunga Lunga. Mama Bendettah and the *"Nikumbuke* women" picked white and blue for the new colors, and starting growing plants and vegetation "For the Center to look sweet and smart," as they said. The same year, 2012, Dr. Abdulcadir Sido, a 72 year-old dentist from the Madison area in Wisconsin, recently retired, and originally from Somalia, joined the N-HbM team and made it his call "Not only to pull teeth but also to treat and restore, to prevent decay, and to train locals in basic dental care and hygiene."

### Permanent Dentist Unit: Building Healthy Smiles

The waiting queue was endless—women, men and children from the seven villages and beyond waited infinite hours to be seen by Dr. Sido. The news that a free dentist would be working in Lunga Lunga during the months of May and June ran very fast and spread around the region. Mama Bendettah had to organize a system of appointments so that people would not have to wait long hours outside the clinic. The need and the desire to be seen, however, overrode any potential organization and people with appointment and no appointment arrived at the Center before sunrise and remained at the door of the clinic until they were seen, even past sunset. Nurse Josephine and the new apprentice in the office, Mr. Wilson Nyae, assisted Dr. Sido while being trained on basic dental care.

The presence of a "black man from America whose tribe is Somali," as women introduced Dr. Sido to the communities, became an interesting case study as he broke all the imaginable stereotypes to the women. On the one hand, Dr. Sido was very rigorous, serious, and meticulous in his work. On the other hand he was very gentle, friendly, compassionate, accessible and open to talk with his patients not only about teeth but also about all kinds of taboo subjects with a natural familiarity—menstrual cramps, breastfeeding positions, "feminine itching," and even sexuality. When the women inquired about his openness to discuss such matters, he answered calmly: "I am the father of seven daughters, married to a very liberal French lady, and I am used to discuss all these things as simple matters at the dinner table."

"But, you are a Muslim!" the women reminded Dr. Sido.

"And you're from the Somali tribe," they continued.

"Yes, but my wife is Jewish, she is white, and my eight children came in all colors and religions. Nowadays, some of my grown kids and grandkids are Jewish, some are Christian, and some are Muslim. Beyond tribes, beyond colors, beyond religions, we are all people, and as humans and we have more similarities than differences," Dr. Sido said.

The definitive acceptance of Dr. Sido's fabulous and extraordinary openness towards women's health issues came during an all-village celebration when the women requested Dr. Sido to dance in front of a huge crowd, to what he responded with a Somali *Niiko* dance, moving his hips back and forth and up and down; the women cheered, clapped, cried of laughter, and imitated his fabulous moves. After that first time in 2012, he has been asked to dance over and over again; after all, the women know that Dr. Sido will brighten and boost any gathering of people with his extraordinary sense of humor and humanity.

Again, with every gain a new challenge emerged. In 2012, Dr. Sido had carried with him an inventory of dental care supplies to last for several hundred patients, but before he completed two weeks of work the materials were gone and he had to do dentistry work as he had never thought he would: using warm salt water for rinsing, a bucket for spitting blood, boiling water to sterilize materials, placing temporary fillings made of cotton or even chewing gum until he could get more permanent ones. Soon, doing dentistry in the area would become a tremendous challenge for Dr. Sido: a massive number of patients with tooth decay, abscesses, gum disease, cavities in baby teeth, mouth sores, tooth injuries, and all of that complicated with high rates of HIV infection and high mortality associated with AIDS.

Dr. Sido's dental unit helped prevent, diagnose and treat common teeth and mouth problems for these underserved communities. Dr. Sido's dental unit also helped us understand the relativity of things problematizing the meaning of "underserved":

"Could Dr. Sido see me today?" This inquiry did not come from the women of Lunga Lunga or from any of the women around the area but from one of my students from the United States. "I've never seen a dentist before in my life" the student confessed, "and I'd like to see one; I'm curious about my teeth and my mouth." This student who was privileged in the context of the Kenyan rural world, had been unprivileged in her own country and unable to be covered by health insurance. As many families in the United States, her parents were low-income and uninsured; the student had not visited the dentist not because she did not need it but because she could not afford it. The women from Lunga Lunga were puzzled. From their vantage point, it was not easy to understand that a young woman from "America" waited for so long to see a dentist, and finally saw one in a remote and isolated area of rural Kenya; a dentist who came from the same town in "America" as the student, a dentist who happened to be working for free those days in Lunga Lunga.

### "Train the Trainers" Program

The women from the same villages of Lunga-Lunga, Godo and Perani where the Summer Health Camps were conducted in 2010, insisted in repeating the camps the following year. Training 300 women, however, posed some difficulties in terms of resources and sustainability. Again, we listened to the wishes of the women, but to make health training successful in 2011, we would need to make some changes in the program, not only to maximize resources but also to guarantee sustainability and ownership; in the end, lasting change had to come from within, from the women themselves; removing ourselves from the role of "teachers" would benefit the women in their roles of producers and reproducers of knowledge.

The new 2011 health program would be based on the training of a small number of women who after the training would become "health promoters" or community health workers, and who in turn would train other women during the year multiplying the basic health knowledge by hundreds, even by thousands. The newly born health promoters would hold village meetings or "health parties" with other women in their own communities and would discuss health issues and health concerns specific of each group; each pair of promoters committed to hold one health party per month.

The first cohort of women health promoters was selected by the leaders of each community, based on their commitment to help others, desire to learn, and also basic literacy in Kiswahili and English. Three villages participated—Lunga Lunga, Godo, and Perani. The leaders selected four women from each village, and a total of twelve future health promoters attended the training. Planning and control of the health promotion were flexible and responsive to the women's needs and desires since the course content was specifically selected by the community leaders in consultation with the women; as a result, what was taught matched the community's needs and desires. Although the group of health promoters was ethnically very diverse, it was small enough—only twelve—for everyone to know each other.[18] The main responsibility of the women health promoters was three fold: 1) disseminate the information learned in the training; 2) assess the health needs of women in their communities; 3) inform

---

[18] The first year, the twelve health promoters belonged to the Kamba, Digo, Duruma, Luhya and Giriama ethnic groups, and practiced Christianity and Islam in almost equal numbers.

regularly the staff of N-HbAM in its headquarters of Lunga Lunga. Those twelve health promoters would have to work together during the year, reporting to the local Director of the projects, and community leader, Madam Bendettah Muthina. Mama Bendettah, in consultation with nurse Josephine Matini and with me, would decide the next steps: whether to develop further programs, create new interventions or revise the existing ones.

During the five years of implementation, the Train the Trainers approach constantly evolved and adapted to meet women's changing wants and needs, helping the women to become more self-confident about their own capacity for effective decision making and action. For example, the first two years the women health promoters preferred to work in other neighboring villages instead of in their own; they claimed that it was difficult for them to be seen with authority in their own villages: "I am just a house-wife, a Mama, and everybody knows me as such," "I can't be listened to as a knowledgeable health promoter in my village all of a sudden," "Nobody would want to listen to me!" several Mamas said and the others agreed. Two years after the first training, however, in 2013 the health promoters felt confident enough to advocate in their own villages and we applauded their decision since it was our belief that by working in their own communities the health promoters were helping break the cycle of dependency from outside.

As the health promoters continued their work through the year, other villages requested to train their leaders. In 2012 five villages participated—Lunga Lunga, Godo, Perani, Mpakani and Jirani. The year of 2013 saw a tremendous advancement in the number of villages participating with the addition of two Maasai communities—Maasailand and Umoja. The number of villages was not the greatest advancement, however; the most unexpected innovation of that year would be the incorporation of a man to the cohort of women health promoters. In the village of Maasailand, Mama Rose in the name of the village leaders requested that her son, Isack Ngunzo, be trained as the first health promoter of the village. Two reasons were given by Mama Rose: 1) Isack was among the very few to speak Kiswahili in addition to the Maa language, and 2) Isack wanted it! Contrary to expectations, stereotypes and assumptions about the patriarchal nature of Maasai men, Isack wanted to be a health promoter and advocate for women's health and for community health.

At the end of the first "train the trainers" program in 2011, the teaching team realized that the women were chattering about *mtihani*, test or testing. The last day of the training the women were given diplomas for their learning without being tested first, assuming that "testing" would be a coercive western imposition. "But how do we know that they have learned?" Mama Bendettah asked us. Interestingly, by trying to avoid an imposition from the West, we were already imposing our own westernized and paternalistic assumptions that considered those women incapable to be tested about their newly acquired knowledge. After consulting with the health promoters and the women leaders, we all agreed that testing was not only fair but also desired by the health promoters; the only challenge would be to develop culturally sensitive questions in accordance with the language and the literacy level of each woman. Because the number of health promoters was small, even smaller than the teaching team, the following year 2012 we devoted the time to prepare pre and post-tests tailored individually for each health promoter in training. For example, one health promoter insisted in taking the test in English since it was important for her to do it that way. Another health promoter, however, preferred to take the test in Kiswahili, and another one needed a person who could read the questions and record the answers. The pre and post-tests allowed the teaching team to assess, not only women's learning capacity but also the efficacy of our own teaching styles and materials, and also our own competency to share and translate knowledges and ways of knowing. The health promoters were tested on health issues that they had wanted to learn in the first place: communicable diseases, nutrition, maternal health, sexual transmitted infections and diseases, water-borne illnesses, hygiene, reproductive health, cancer of the reproductive female organs, etc. Through their formal testing, the women chose to prove that they were ready to fulfill their task as the future health trainers of other women from their communities. After that moment, and acknowledging their big responsibility as health promoters, nurse Josephine decided to test the women every six months to make sure their knowledge was still accurate, otherwise they would need to attend instructional workshops to refresh their health information.

Health Promoters studying their notes during summer health camp "Train the Trainers". Photo by HbM Team.

### *Maasai Train the Trainers*

Many of the women from non-Maasai villages—Lunga Lunga, Mpakani, Godo, Perani, Jirani—had been hesitant to include Maasai women within the N-HbM framework. The Maasai women "dress differently," "eat different food," and celebrate "different" rites of passage. They are "difficult" and "stubborn," far too "set in their ways." The Maasai, too, were hesitant to work with N-HbM. While some members of the Maasai communities of Umoja and Maasailand had directly requested to be part of N-HbM, others were more cautious. This seemed to be rather common throughout Kenya; in fact, Madam Bendettah mentioned that a government official had asked her why she would even consider working with Maasai tribes, citing their "reluctance to change" as an obstacle that apparently could not be overcome.

In his book, *The Moral Imagination: The Art and Soul of Building Peace*, Paul Lederach (2005) mentions the ability to transcend a narrow "reality" as one of the greatest tools for peace building. This ability is what he calls the "moral imagination" that opens up human potentialities for action beyond what is immediately apparent, opening humans to the possibility of creative acts towards peace building. It seemed as if the women from all these villages had read Lederach's words when he writes:

> Stated simply, the moral imagination requires the capacity to imagine ourselves in a web of relationships that includes our enemies; the ability to sustain a paradoxical curiosity that embraces complexity without reliance on dualistic polarity; the fundamental belief in and pursuit of the creative act; and the acceptance of the inherent risk of stepping into the mystery of the unknown that lies beyond the far too familiar landscape of violence. (Lederach, 2005: 5)

Indeed, the participation of Maasai women and of Chief Isack Ngunzo in the Train the Trainers was a breakthrough in the program that transcended the narrow reality apparent to us observers, and opened up potentials for creative acts that went beyond our understandings. Furthermore, it meant an "outreach success" since the Maasai communities were located in the most isolated and ostracized of all areas. It also meant a "unity success" in the sense that health was again a concept that united different tribes that had not shared common grounds before. As a result of prejudices and deeply entrenched stereotypes, the Maasai and other tribes had rarely mingled; the Maasai were regarded by other groups as "backwards, dirty, odd" and the Maasai perceived the other communities as their potential adversaries. Besides, the participation of Isack Ngunzo in the health training program meant a "gender shift" since it was the first time that men were not just hesitant observers of their wives' work but participants in the construction of healthier communities for all. Moreover, allowing one of the young men to join a group of only-women health promoters on women's health issues by another group of only-women trainers, was a revolutionary decision taken by the elder men of Maasailand.

Needless to say, having Isack Ngunzo for the Train the Trainers was taken with caution by the women and with indecision by the teaching team from UW-Madison. On the one hand, the dynamic of the group could be in jeopardy; the women had always felt safe sharing their most intimate health concerns and having a man, regardless of his tribe, could threaten the learning environment for all. On the other hand, the presence of Isack was seen by Mama Joyce, another Maasai woman from Umoja, as "our men wanting to be in control... once again!" as she put it.

Language also became a challenge for the training considering that Maasai speak their own Maa language and very few people in these Maasai communities speak Kiswahili or English. Isack spoke Kiswahili but the Maasai women only spoke Maa and we needed an interpreter English-Kiswahili-Maa since there was no one who could interpret directly from English to Maa.

The Train the Trainers of 2013 came to an end, and regardless all the challenges, we could all attest that the presence of Maasai women and of Isack among the women were a complete asset and a confirmation that something was happening in the communities, including the Maasai villages. The Maasai women and Isack were excellent team players, listeners, followers, and also leaders when appropriate. The women from other tribes opened up in front of Isack and the Maasai women in ways that we could not have anticipated; they were not only comfortable talking about maternal health, hygiene, nutrition, or infectious diseases but also about taboo topics never discussed before—anal sex, oral sex, FGC, violence against girls and women, rape. At the end of the training, Isack stood up in front of all, trainers and trainees, thanked all for the learning opportunity and claimed that he was committed to advocate for women's health and to end violence against girls and women in his community, "no more Maasai girls will be raped while I am a community leader," he said.

Throughout the year, Isack became even more pro-active than some of the women health promoters of the same cohort. He created a school for girls and boys in Maasailand and started teaching the children alphabetization but also girls' health, gender equality, and the importance of education. Not satisfied with his work and eager to learn more and recycle his knowledge, the following year 2014, Isack requested to be retrained as a health promoter. His example became a role model for other Maasai men and women. In addition to Isack, in 2014 three more Maasai requested the training: Isack's 14 year-old sister-in-law Maria who was pregnant at the time, Mama Joyce Pius from Umoja who had attended the training in 2013 but requested to retake it, and Isaya Muringa, another young man from Umoja who asked to be a health promoter, probably influenced by a recent event in which Mama Joyce had been involved.

Just a few months before the training, Isaya's second wife gave birth to her first son but after the delivery she did not stop bleeding. Maternal and infant death is something well known among the Maasai. Although the women are very strong and give birth with no fuss, if there is a complication such as placenta previa, obstructive labor or incomplete placental birth, the death of the mother or of the baby, or the death of both, are almost inevitable. The bleeding did not stop for Isaya's wife and transporting her to the hospital from Umoja village was unthinkable at such stage. Mama Joyce was called to intervene.

"I didn't know what to do, but I remembered something from the training of the former year that was about rubbing the nipples and pushing out like urinating, and putting the baby in the breast while the other nipple was rubbed. We repeated that. It was frightening, but the insides of her came out and after a while the blood stopped coming." Isaya's baby and wife survived and Isaya decided to become a health promoter.

The process of incorporating Maasai to the train-the-trainers and to all the programs of N-HbM was not easy, though, and challenges started surfacing as the Maasai communities began to change. For example, the elder women of Maasailand protested because "Isack is talking to us about things that bring shame to us," such as sexually transmitted infections or cervical cancer. "We can't even listen to him without blushing!" one of the women objected. Isack's desire, however, has not been informed only by his training in health promotion but by his genuine desire to bring the status of girls and women up, regardless of facing criticism in his community.

Isack went further; he was truly concerned about the dangers of cutting the clitoris to the girls and about the rapid spread of HIV among some Maasai communities. Isack became in charge of a difficult task: making sure that the girls attended school. The Maasai girls of Maasailand and Umoja had never gone to school, their mothers were illiterate and the girls faced the same fate. Isack, however, was committed to change that and through N-

HbM's system of scholarships he started managing to make his dream come true and have the girls in school. One of Isack's bold actions was to give identity to the girls by officially issuing birth certificates to all who started attending school. Because of the amount of girls who needed birth certificates, a government official traveled to Maasailand to issue the certificates instead of asking all the girls to go to the nearest city. Since the Maasai from Maasailand live in isolation and are still semi-nomadic, the birth certificates could have been easily avoided, but Isack's desire was that all the girls in his community have a legal status. Isack proved to think long-term with specific initiatives for his Maasai community.

Tribal differences, however, continued to be somewhat of an obstacle for N-HbM's programs, as they were in much of the country. As Charles Hornsby (2001) said, ethnicity in Kenya is "about shared communities... but also about conflict and difference" (2). Hornsby argues that politics and social organizations in Kenya cannot be understood without a strong knowledge of ethnicity. In that way, working with the Maasai has brought about a unique way to recognize social justice and human rights to the N-HbM team, acknowledging the claim that the Maasai community has suffered from marginalization since Kenya was a British colony (Ole Simel 2004).

In 1904 and 1911, with the Anglo-Maasai treaties the Maasai were forcibly removed from their fertile lands and driven to dry, southern reserves such as the eastern border with Tanzania where Maasailand is located and where the habitat was harsh and largely unsustainable. It was estimated that the Maasai lost 75 percent of their land to the colonial government through a treaty that was unclear and full of irregularities, but which had been used to argue that the Maasai somehow voluntarily gave up their land (Ole Simel 2004) This is a claim that Maasai leaders continue to contest today.

When Kenya gained its independence, the new government was quick to adopt foreign colonial legal systems, including English property laws, thus legitimizing the removal of the Maasai from their land (Ole Simel 2004). According to Meitamei Olol-Dapesh (2011), despite their best efforts, independence did not bring about the return of the estimated six million hectares of land that had been taken from the Maasai people. With the arrival of neoliberalism, land increasingly became a commodity to be hoarded, marketed, and sold, and Maasai land continued to be appropriated through corruption and annexed in the name of national interest, all without the knowledge of the Maasai people (Olol-Dapesh 2001). Today, Maasai land has been designated for large-scale agriculture, military installations, hydroelectric dams, and tourism, leaving little hope that it will ever be returned to the hands of the Maasai.

Dispossession of their land was devastating for Maasai people, not only economically but also culturally. For the Maasai, land is a source of livelihood and cultural heritage that is to be preserved for future generations. Under Maasai custom law, there is no such thing as private property. Land is owned, managed, and controlled collectively, and it is impossible for a single individual or group of people to give away that land to anyone (Ole Simel 2004). The Maasai pastoral way of living has become unattainable under land subdivisions that do not recognize their cultural way of life.

In Maasailand, years of marginalization and a constant silencing has led to the drastic impoverishment of the community; their Maa language has been threatened, as has the existence of the entire community. They are losing their culture due to lack of a land base, low self-esteem and increased vulnerability and discrimination. For Kenyan society, the Maasai have become a "nuisance" in light of assimilationist and integrationist policies, as they are regarded as anti-development, difficult, and too resistant to change.

"Not only boys will get educated in Maasailand," Isack announced at the end of the train-the-trainers in 2014, and in 2015 his commitment paid off, as a group of 25 Maasai girls of different ages started attending primary school divided into three boarding institutions. Several issues had to be considered, though. First, sending the Maasai girls to school was not going to solve the structural violence and the poverty created by decades of exploitation in capitalist development. Second, the girls would have to be closely monitored to cover all their needs and not just school fees—school uniforms, books, meals, etc.; recruiting girls and paying their fees to school was not good enough to keep the girls attending school regularly. Third, the girls would need to develop a hard skin to endure the bullying coming from girls from other ethnic groups, which they did! By the end of 2016, all 25 girls could read and write in Kiswahili and they were becoming proficient in English.

Maasai women from Maasailand singing in gratitude for health training.
Photo by Liliane Calfee.

Another challenge, though, would be to make sure that the girls would not end up rejecting their Maasai upbringing or forgetting their Maa language. Going to school was for the girls a way to acquire more gender equality with the Maasai boys, but not to walk away from their culture. Just the opposite, Isack's intention of sending the girls to school was to prepare the next generation of nurses and teachers to work in the Maasai communities. Besides, "government would not mess [up] with us if our girls and boys are well educated and know how to read and write" Isack said.

### *Playing, Dancing: Beach, Celebrations*

Since 2011, we started celebrating the equator of the health promotion training by going to the beach. The teaching team from UW-Madison, the new cohort of health promoters and the staff of N-HbM spend an entire day together at Diane Beach in Ukunda, around 15 kilometers from Lunga Lunga where the training took place. This celebration became a rite of passage for all. The days at the beach were probably the most memorable of all. Most of the women had never been at a beach before and the excitement was always high. Some of them were dismayed seeing the water coming inland and getting to them, wondering why the water was contained within the limits of the sea and did not invade the surrounding villages.

Our beach days started around 7 am at the Nikumbuke Community Health Center with the women trying bathing suits on and deciding which one fit their body type the best; they giggled first and soon started laughing louder and louder. "I'm not wearing this!" one of the health promoters said almost chocking, to what Mama Bendettah would respond with her authoritarian voice "These are our uniforms for the day! Our health promoters' uniforms for the day!" They all laughed even louder. In a tiny room there were around fifteen women, sharing the parts of their bodies that they so prudently covered in the outside world. It was obvious that they were having a blast. The women were not laughing about their bodies or anybody else's bodies; they were laughing *with* their bodies. Some of these women had their own difficult challenges: two were HIV+; another was a third wife and had just been rejected by her husband, losing custody of her two children; another barely survived malaria the previous month; another had a daughter that had been taken to Mombasa "to work at a hotel," but she knew well what kind of a place was that hotel. All the women, however, as they tried their bathing suits, seemed to have their sorrows suspended.

When the Maasai joined the Train the Trainers, some of us were apprehensive thinking about their reaction towards coming to the beach. I thought they surely would not come. Once again, our own prejudices, stereotypes, and partial knowledge gave us a limited understanding of human behavior and made us assume that the Maasai were peculiar, strange, atypical people. The Maasai came, all of them; every single year they came. The Maasai women did not behave in any way differently from the other women, they wore bathing suits, even Mama Joyce selected a bikini for her but also wore her red and white *chukka* on top. Isack and Isaya wore blue shorts under their red *chukkas*.

Regardless of our bathing suits, regardless of our myriad skin tones, of our different body abilities, body types and shapes, regardless of our cultures, our languages, our challenges, our desires, in spite of all our separations we all found unity and attachment through an uncontrollable eagerness for enjoyment; a state of frenzy captured us all as we approached the beach. None of the health promoters knew how to swim, but it did not matter, since swimming was not the purpose of our field trip. Some feared the water, but some did not. Some got into the water without thinking, while others practiced a preparatory swimming lesson laying face down on the sand and moving their legs and arms while the observers burst in choking laughter. We all came into the water screaming and jumping, intoxicated with happiness and living a surreal experience. We were loud, very loud. We played together, with each other and with ourselves, laughing until we were exhausted, swallowing water as we were laughing and chasing each other. We invented games: blindfolded, one of us would shout *Twiga!* giraffe! while chasing the others as they screamed *Simba!* Lion! *Twiga! Simba! Twiga! Simba!* When we were exhausted, we came out of the water, ate together, played volleyball together, walked around the shore together. At the beach, we lost any former trait of identity as we unleashed the power of unity, the plenitude of oneness.

### *Street Health Theater* Afya Ukumbi

At the beginning of 2012, almost one year after the first Train the Trainers health promotion program, a group of women from Lunga Lunga took the genuine initiative of performing "dramas," as they call their acting, taking the subversive Harvard's Pre-Texts pedagogy into their own hands[19]. The women used their inner knowing and motivated by the knowledge acquired through the training of the previous summer. Although the UW team had nothing to do with this impulse of the women to perform, the new knowledge might have acted as a catalyst for the women to share the treasured information in a culturally more appropriate way.

The women developed the scripts, collected the garments, rehearsed for several months and in June of 2012 eleven women

---

[19] The Pre-Texts is a pedagogy protocol created by Professor Doris Sommer, Ira and Jewell Williams Professor of Romance Languages and Literatures and of African and African American Studies at Harvard University, and Director of the Cultural Agents Initiative at Harvard University. The Pre-Texts pedagogy uses a combination of creative interpretation and reflection techniques—dancing, body movement, music, theater, written texts, etc. to achieve high levels of cognitive and emotional development and holistic education.

starred as female actors performing in the streets of Lunga Lunga in front of several hundred people, including our UW-Madison team. Although only one out of the eleven women actors had basic skills in reading and writing, the lack of literacy was not a constraint to advocate for women's health and to change community's perception of health and disease; acting gave women a platform to discuss how different factors could help or hinder health, and explain specific implications of healthy lifestyles and habits. The genuine desire of women for advancing health in their communities led them to the formation of what Sloman (2012) called Theater for Development. It was as if the women had been mysteriously inspired by the theories of Brazilian educators and activists Paulo Freire (1970) and Augusto Boal (1979, 1995) as they started integrating health education and entertainment to construct not only a healthier society but also community cohesion and peace building platform (for more details see Figure 2).

The first drama was non-participatory in the sense that there was no interaction between the female actors and the public; the women acted the play in a didactic way while the audience listened and watched, mesmerized as the health information was sinking in their souls. Although non-participatory, this first drama could be understood as one of the forms of what Boal (1979) denominated "Theater of the Oppressed," in which performers enact their plays in places where people do not expect to see any kind of public acting. This first malaria play was performed in the streets of Lunga Lunga where several hundred surprised people gathered around forming a gigantic circle to witness what Boal would have called "Invisible Theater."

First act of the malaria play: a pregnant woman and her husband are sleeping on a mattress, without a net. The crowd bursts in laughter when Mama Damaris, dressed as a mosquito, appears in the scene buzzing around the pregnant Mama while she is asleep. The mosquito bites the Mama who starts feeling sick. When the Mama cannot stand on her own, her husband takes her to a traditional witch doctor that performs rituals and starts dancing and singing frantically around the woman. The crowd could not contain itself, rejoicing with every histrionic movement of the witchdoctor. The couple goes back home, but the Mama does not improve. When the husband finally decides to take his wife to the clinic, it is too late to save her or the baby; both died. The spectators looked at each other with complicit gestures, unfortunately recognizing the scene and related it to their own lives. Applauses! Second act: The same pregnant woman with the same husband sleeping under a blue net. The mosquito comes again and the crowd yells and cries out *Unaweza si!* (You can't!). Mama Damaris in her big mosquito dress tries several times but the net interferes and the pregnant Mama cannot be bitten; eventually the mosquito dies while the observers scream in victory and congratulate the Mama for sleeping under the net, *Hongera! Hongera!*

For our UW team, observing this malaria skit meant much more than anyone could have anticipated; it was a fantastic demonstration of the way the health promotion training of the previous summer had been incorporated into the acting, further-more into daily life. The fact that the Mama did not die meant that the health promoters and the performers had perfectly understood that *Plasmodium falciparum* infections in pregnant women who live in malaria endemic areas, like Kwale County, have a direct risk for infant mortality rather than for maternal mortality (Steketee et al. 2001).

At the end of 2012, the women and the UW-Madison team decided to establish the Street Health Theater as one of the permanent programs of N-HbM; thanks to a grant from the UW-Madison Morgridge Center, the *Afya Ukumbi* or Street Health Theater was born. Since 2012, the number of performers has grown dramatically because other villages wanted to do the same. Godo was performing, Perani was performing, Jirani was performing as well. Each village, except the two Maasai communities which express their learning through songs instead of through theater, were acting health dramas. The groups of female actors incorporated skits based on all the health promotion workshops: maternal health, infections diseases, HIV/AIDS, and even domestic violence and the trafficking of girls. In sum, the women created dramas that reflected their own health struggles, problems, and experiences within their communities. Kwale women understood that using theater, also singing and dancing, arts in general would eventually help them solve real-life challenges.

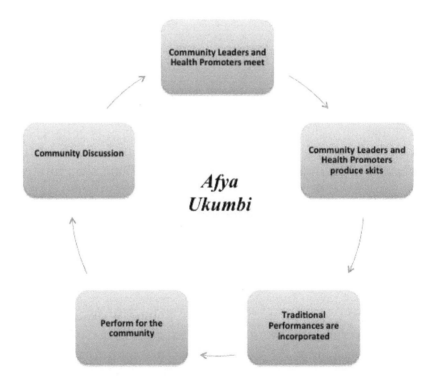

**Figure 2.** *Afya Ukumbi* mechanism of action.

The *Afya Ukumbi* has been a good example of what Doris Sommer (2014) calls the utility of arts and humanities in civil engagement. In her book, *The Work of Art in the World* (2014), Sommer explains how bottom up artistic expression and creative elements, unconventional activities for some, like the *Afya Ukumbi*, can create powerful dynamics of social change and hence play an essential role in promoting political participation and even in changing the status quo. The *Afya Ukumbi* has become a provocative and fun tool for civic education, health promotion and social justice; a subversive means to provoke, confront and interrogate spectators, but also to unify, celebrate and heal audiences and communities.

In 2013, N-HbM women made the *Afya Ukumbi* more participatory, asking the audience to collaborate after the play and analyze it all together step by step, giving rise to a form of Forum Theater (Boal, 1979) in which the audience would eventually become "spect-actors", as Boal called it, allowing knowledge and learning to flow reciprocally between actors and spect-actors. This new approach helped initiate reflection and discussion about solutions to past, present, and potential health problems. The ultimate purpose of the new participatory *Afya Ukumbi* was to conceive action through solidarity and community consciousness; that happened already at the end of 2013 when the Lunga Lunga *Afya Ukumbi* performers, after watching and analyzing a four-minute play created by the UW team, decided to perform skits on intimate domestic disputes, a subject that had been completely taboo until then. The four-minute piece that sparked the desire to perform on domestic disputes was a play acted in Kiswahili by one of my senior students and by myself. After much self-reflection and work within, the student and I put ourselves out there in front of the women, acting from the inside out, embracing and sharing our own vulnerability.

Husband:    *Hodi, Hodi*
            (Knock, knock; greeting to enter the house)

Wife:       *Karibu, Karibu sana*
            (Come in, welcome; greeting to get into the house)

Husband:    *Umeshindaje?*
            How is everything?

Wife:       *Salama, Salama*
            Fine, fine

To our surprise, the women burst into laughter seeing the two wazungu[20] women speaking and acting in Kiswahili.

Husband:    *Nimeleta nyama leo.*
            I am bringing meat today.

Wife:       *Nyama choma, nyama choma. Asante sana,
            asante sana mume yangu.*

            *Mimi ni bibi mzuri. Mimekubali makosa yangu
            yete ambato yalisababaisha kunipiga usiku.
            Nitabadilisha tabia ynagu na kwa mke mzuri.*

            Oh, meat, meat, thank you so much my husband. I'll
            be a good wife. I deserved to be beaten last night
            but I'll be good.

The women were not laughing anymore.

Husband:    *Nimekusameje, nimekusameje. Chakula kiko
            tayari?*

            I forgive you, I forgive you. Is the food ready?

---

[20] Wazungu is the plural form of mzungu, a word that the locals used to refer to "white people."

Wife:         *Ndyo! Nimetayarisha ugali na kuku.*
              Yes! I prepared ugali[21] and chicken.

Husband:      *Watoto wako wapi?*
              Where are our children?

Wife:         *Minewakeleka kwa nayana yao!*
              I've taken them to their grandmother.

Husband:      *Unasema nini!!!????*
              What!!!!????
              *Nimekwanbia usiwapeleke watoto wangu kwa mama yako?*
              How can I tell you not to take the children to your mother?

Wife:         *Nisemehe mume wangu. Siturudia tena.*
              I am so sorry my husband, forgive me.

Husband:      *Wewe nimkinga sana!!!*
              You are so stupid!!!

              *Lete chakula haraka!*
              Bring me the food!

Wife:         *Haya, mumu wangu. Chakula hiki hapa.*
              Here you have, my husband. Here is the food.

Husband:      *Ugali iko baridi!! Kuku imeungua!! Nimara ngapi nimekupiga na bado hujarekebisha tabia yako?*
              The ugali is cold, the chicken is burned! How many times have I beat you and you have not adjusted your character?

(He violently hits her and leaves the house)

---

[21] A semi-hard cake made of maize flour or millet flour. It is a staple food, the favorite meal for all Kenyans to accompany fish, meat, beans, stews, vegetables, etc.

Although completely unintentional, it seemed that by making ourselves vulnerable, the student and I had made a space for the women to open up. That play gave rise to an "aesthetic space," as Boal (1995) would name it, a liminal zone where reality and fiction converged in one single universe. Through the physicality of acting out this play in Kiswahili, women in the audience who in daily life were silent became protagonists on the stage, and their feelings of oppression became as tangible and solid as our own bodies. It was within that liminal space where everything became possible, where transformation took place between what "it was" and the "next."

It took four minutes and four questions for the women to feel a tight knot in their guts, a sense a deep inner pain, but also a sudden urgency to speak and act out. The audience became activated spect-actors, and I took the role of the "Joker," as Augusto Boal (1995) called the facilitator of the Forum Theater:

"Is this the fault of the Mama? Is the Mama stupid?"
I asked.

"Noooooooo!!!!!!" The women shouted as loud as they could.

"Why does the husband bring chicken?"

"Because *kuku* is sweet[22]; he wants to be forgiven, but he is not saying the truth, he is not repented and does it again and again."
"Why are the children at the grandma's place?"
"Because the Mama doesn't want her children to see what is going on in the house."

"Do you think the *ugali* is cold and the chicken burned?
"Noooooooo!!!!!!"

---

[22] In this context the word "sweet" refers to a most delicious food. Also, locals use the word "sweet" to refer to something beautiful, to a very pretty person; "sweet" is used as synonymous of "best."

The conversation started being run by the women, challenging one another, asking and answering to each other, shouting, crying, deciphering the legacy and evils of a patriarchal system where violence against women takes many forms and is normalized in everyday life; and the conversation continued for hours:

"No man has the right to beat his wife"

"Beating is not love, it's violence!"

"Isn't it violence also when your husband brings home another woman and you have to sleep on the floor while they sleep in the bed and then in the morning you have to prepare chapati[23] and chai[24] for them?"

"Isn't it violence when your husband keeps all the money for himself leaving you and your children with nothing?"

"Isn't it violence when your husband forces you every night? And if you don't do it he takes the children and you are in the street!"

"What about when your husband ignores you sexually?"

"And when the girls are cut? Isn't that violence?"

"And when your baby is the son of your uncle and you cannot talk because he would kill you? And then you tell no one because no one believes you anyway and people would blame you and your family would kick you out".

"And when a woman only gives birth to girls and her husband takes a second wife to have sons with her?"

"Women are blamed and beaten for having too many kids, or for not having kids at all, isn't that violence too?"

"Not letting a woman to have family planning; that's violence!!

"And when a woman overstays in the market and her

---

[23] Chapati is a round, flat unleavened bread cooked on a griddle to a soft brown color. It can be eaten alone or with meat, beans, stews and vegetables.

[24] Chai is the typical Kenyan tea prepared with milk.

husband beats her up when she gets home?"

"Some men take drugs and cannot get satisfied and force women and the women get hurt, they try the anus and the vagina, and over again".

"After having a baby, men don't want to wait the six weeks and demand sex to their wives right away, I think that's violence"

"When a woman is sick, she is the last one to be taken to the hospital until her illness kills her, that's violence because she dies".

The atmosphere got tenser as the women turned the conversation into a discussion on rape and sexual violence. It was then when one of my own students stood up and said: "I was raped when I was 18, the first year of my studies at the University of Wisconsin-Madison; this is the first time I speak about it." Another student intervened: "I was 20 when I was raped on campus. I thought it was my fault because I was drunk, I never told anyone." A total of four out of my twelve students confessed there, in front of the women, being raped on our own campus. The silence became thicker than ever, until one of the women, a spect-actor, asked: "So, rape happens in America too?"

The women, my students, everyone, could perceive the complex global web of women's oppression, but we also started realizing that anyone can become an agent of change. Two more hours of discussion on gender-based violence concluded in a giant human circle where all of us, standing up and holding hands, praying in silence first and later voicing our commitments to ending violence against women and girls.

The same year, before 2013 ended, the Jirani *Afya Ukumbi* group of female actors went a step further performing a drama on structural and gender-based violence inflicted on girls. In the play, a girl gives up going to school due to a cascade of facts and events: lack of money to pay school fees, lack of sanitary pads for the days of her period, lack of time because she has to fetch water, fear of rape if she walks alone to school, fear of her father who disapproves her going to school and beat her up, fear of her mother being beaten for allowing her to go to school, more fear of her father when he gets drunk. Although the play presented a real drama, the performers found a way to make the audience laugh. The viewers could identify themselves with the play as the reflection of a mirror; the laughter, however, diminished the pain, increased intimacy and strengthened community engagement and cohesiveness.

The female actors took every bit of information given during the health promotion program, every common knowledge, every cultural belief and converted them, translated them into a drama adapting it to the specific circumstances of each community. For example, when the Lunga Lunga actors performed their drama on HIV, the whole audience cracked-up as a Mama tried to convince her husband to use a condom. Condoms were unknown in the villages before 2010 and although they were still seen as something not desirable, thanks to the *Afya Ukumbi* more and more people were demystifying them. In the play, the Mama insisted to her uncooperative husband that he put a condom before engaging in intercourse. The husband rejects the condom several times claiming that "This is only for prostitutes! *Mimi ni mwanaume*! I am a man! You don't dare to give me this" "You do what I say!" The Mama, however, did not appear intimidated but neither she pushed her husband to do something he did not like or want. On the contrary, the Mama was using all her skills for him to change his mind, showing him how to put the condom on and even telling him that she could try to do it with her mouth; the spect-actors did not look embarrassed or ashamed, or showed any discontent or disapproval of the women's audacity and insolence. The audience seemed mesmerized and laughed harder and louder as the Mama tried to put the condom on a wooden penis attached to the "husband's" pants. The Mama did not mention HIV to her husband at all, neither she mentioned that she was trying to protect herself from other sexually transmitted infections or from unwanted pregnancies. The Mama was presenting the condom to her husband as something desirable for his own enjoyment.

*Afya Ukumbi* women actors performing a "drama" on maternal and neo-natal health. Photo by HbM Team.

Through the medium of performance and storytelling, community health promoters turned into actors freely expressing the particular health issues that affected their communities. The *Afya Ukumbi* intelligently used laughter as a subversive language to discuss sensitive health topics, contest structural violence, and even reverse gender roles. Besides, laughter brought people together, acting as a great unifier and creating an atmosphere of acceptance among groups of different ethnic backgrounds and religions, thus allowing performers to reach marginalized groups in their communities.

## The Rafiki *Club, Phone Texting and Social Media as Literacy Programs*

The *Rafiki* Club had given birth to the whole movement of N-HbM that started with the two simple letters that Mariamu and I wrote. That project had been started by another organization that soon closed but that ignited in women the desire to know how to read and write so that they were able to communicate with other women around the world. The idea of the *Rafiki* Club seemed feasible for the University of Wisconsin-Madison with capacity to match university students with women and young girls in the villages of Kwale County. In a mere two months, a student-led organization at the university had trained more than one hundred students that were ready to write their first letters to women and girls in the villages and became pen-pals, *Rafiki*. The organization of the club was not easy, though. Lack of funding for this project forced the women in Kenya to send the letters via email to the students in the United States, while the students sent their letters through ordinary mail to Kenya. Only Madam Bendettah had access to one computer and this new task was occupying a great deal of her time. This same difficulty, however, was what triggered the enthusiasm of the women and girls for learning computer skills and for entering the magic cyber-space. The challenge would be to acquire enough computers to start classes for all interested. In less than two years, though, there were fifteen computers in Lunga Lunga and the women were entering the world of social media. They even talked with the students through Skype.

Another example that increased the desire of women for learning literacy was the acquisition of cell phones. More and more women started owning cell phones, and although the majority of the households had no electricity, those precious devices became a treasure for women who did not mind walking long distances to charge them at local businesses close to the market. The women wanted to write texts to other women, as texting was less expensive than calls and consumed less battery. Having cell phones boosted the desire of the women for reading and writing skills.

### *Water Tanks*

In 2011, while staying at Mama Mariamu's house in Godo the lack of water was pervasive. Drinking water was reduced to a minimum cup of tea in the morning, water for cooking was treasured as the most precious jewel, and water for anything else would often be shared by several of us in the house. Mariamu's two older daughters and myself would use the same small basinet and the same water for our personal hygiene. Mariamu's household would need a minimum of 140 liters, approximately 35 gallons of water per day, 20 liters or 5 gallons for each of the seven members of her family[25]. My own home stay would become a burden for Mariamu if I did not provide my own 20 liters of water per day for my consumption.

During Mariamu's life as a married woman and as a mother, the raining season and the dry seasons, all the seasons, would go by thinking water, talking water, dreaming water, breathing water.

"Wake up, Peninah, Kavata!" Mama Mariamu said, "It's already 4:00!" Those were the only words that broke the savannah's silence every morning. The three younger children were still asleep, and Mariamu's husband was in Mombasa trying

---

[25] According to the WHO, 20 litters per capita per day is considered the minimum amount of water that should be assured to take care of drinking, basic hygiene and basic food preparation. Laundry and bathing might require a higher amount. Wealthy urban dwellers use a minimum of 100 gallons per person per day.

to sell the wood carved figurines he created with few tools and much dedication. It was January, the dry season, when the fields looked all brown and the surface of the earth cracked leaving the outside world like a puzzle of infinite pieces. Peninah 16, Kavata, 14, and their mom had a challenging day ahead of them, as all Godo women and their older daughters did. It all happened in silence, the three women woke up in silence, dressed in silence and at 4:15 slipped out of the house in the same silence. The older, Peninah, pulled the rope of their two oxen; animals also need water.

In their way to the Umba River[26], they meet other neighbor women and girls who also go to fetch water. The Umba River is not close to home. During the rainy season, the women of Godo are luckier because the water pond is only forty minutes away. The water from the pond, however, is muddy and heavily contaminated, as the rainfall rapidly washes away human and animal fecal bacteria down the water source. Many women know that boiling water would kill some of the bacteria, but they are hesitant to boil it since the water is very scarce and in the process of boiling a portion of the water gets lost. But the pond now is completely drained anyhow, and the river is the only choice for the women to fetch water; one hour and thirty minutes away from Mariamu's home, that means a three-hour journey to fetch only 60 liters of water since each of the women can only carry 20 liters over their heads. Some women managed to get bicycles but there is no road to the river and bicycles are often more dangerous than just walking. The worst part of the Umba River is not the distance, though; the water is salty!

When Peninah, Kavata and Mariamu get home with the 60 liters, two of them must return to the river while the third does the chores of the house—sweep the dirt floor inside and outside, wash

---

[26] The Umba River originates in the northeastern part of Tanzania and crosses the border of Kenya before flowing into the Indian Ocean.

the dishes from dinner because in the dark it was difficult to wash; at night there is often no water left to wash, anyhow. She prepares tea, makes flour flatbreads *chapatti*, takes the oxen to the field, cleans the stable of the goats and works in the *chamba* to prepare the fields for the coming rains, weeding the plot and harvesting maize, beans, cowpeas, and ground nuts for their own consumption and hopefully to sell some surplus in the market. The younger ones have gone to school already, Mariamu's eleven-year old daughter is helping her two younger siblings; together, they have to walk five miles to go to school.

At night, the neighbor women come to Mariamu's house. It is 5:00pm and already dark in the savannah. We light the kerosene lamp and we tell stories, we laugh, we look at the same pictures we looked at yesterday, the ones we took last year during the health training, and laugh more, and if there is water we might drink a cup of tea, a salty cup of tea. Mama Margret, Mama Rachel, Mama Molongo, and other Mamas ask me to tell stories about water in "America." I tell them about the basement of my house in Wisconsin flooding because the ground was still frozen to absorb any excess rainwater. They have a hard time thinking about a frozen ground and visualizing a part of the house that is buried, built underground; although having a pool of water underneath their homes sounds appealing to them, we laugh more. "For what purpose it rains in America if Mamas don't collect the water?" Mama Rachel asks. Time to go home, prepare dinner for their families and go to sleep early, to also wake up early to fetch water early and complete another day.

Sometimes the tales and the stories we tell at night have much to do with their back pain; husbands beating their wives for not having enough water to prepare the meals; daughters who want to go to school but cannot because they have to fetch water with their mothers; skin rashes and intestinal parasites because of the lack of proper hygiene; diarrhea for drinking contaminated water collected in the ponds; cholera and other diseases; lack of hygiene for menstruating girls; and the list of tales would go on and on and on.

"In Likoni, I heard that people are using tanks to collect the rain, the water can last for months," Mama Margret said. We discussed the issue together, in Lunga Lunga, in Godo, in Perani: "How would we use rain water tanks in our own benefit?" "How water tanks would benefit our health, the health of our families and of our communities"? The women brainstormed.

At the end of 2011, the first water tank was installed at Mariamu's house, then at Mama Margret's, then Mama Veronica's then Mama Dorcus, and the water tanks kept growing and growing throughout the villages. The system was set up: the university team would fundraise in the United States to purchase the water tanks but the women, the entire family, would have to commit to take care of the tank. Otherwise the tank would be given to another family in need selected by the community leaders. Community leaders, in conversation with the women, would produce a list with the names of those who would receive a water tank as they came. The criteria followed by the leaders consisted on commitment to improve health and life in general for the family and for the community, seriousness and responsibility, family circumstances—number of children, elderly, adults working, family income. The commitment to take good care of the tank would first of all imply for the family to change the *makuti*[27] roof of the house for a tin roof that would permit to connect a water pipe from the roof to the tank. Changing the roof of the house would not only demonstrate commitment but would also become a symbol of prestige and wellness since tin is more expensive than *makuti* and also more permanent; a community with tin roofs indicates affluence and security in the area.

The second stage of commitment required for the family to purchase the water pipe and connect it to the tank. The third stage

[27] Bunches of weaved leaves from coconut plants.

called for the construction of a cement base to support the water tank. N-HbM invests approximately $350 in each 5000-gallon water tank, plus the transportation money from Mombasa to Lunga Lunga in a truck, and from Lunga Lunga to the different villages using any transportation available. The journey of a water tank can be excruciating until reaching its house. A water tank going from Mombasa to Maasailand would require a track, a motorcycle, and for the last kilometers, it would have to be pushed and rolled over until reaching its destination.

For a family that lives with less than $1 a day, purchasing a rainwater tank would be unthinkable. Changing the roof, buying the pipe and connecting it to the roof would still be expensive for most families but that strategy has become decisive for the family to exert and feel ownership over the tank. The communities have come to understand that although the water tanks are given, it is truly the connection of the pipe to the tin roof that makes it possible for the tank to do its function and fill with rainwater to help the family; a water tank is nothing without the effort and commitment of the family.[28]

The ripple effects of the water tanks have been unexpectedly glorious. It was the beginning of July and Mama Margret had not fetched water since early March. Because it was the rain season, Mama Margret and her family "harvested" water from the

---

[28] Each family may select a type of pipe according to affordability or choice. There are three main prices: 250Ksh, around 3.00USD; 800Ksh, approximately 9USD; and 1200Ksh, approximately 13USD. The tin roof also has different prices depending on the size of the house: 680Ksh, approximately 7USD; 890Ksh, approximately 9USD; 980, approximately 10USD; and 1400Ksh, approximately 15USD. The water tank should also use a cement base in order to be protected from the ground. The cement used for the base is about three packets; each packet costs around 750Ksh, approximately 8USD, that is a total of 2250Ksh, approximately 23USD. Additional expenses: sand 1200Ksh, approximately 13USD; stones 1500Ksh, around 16USD. Labor is also paid if the man of the house does not install the tank. This may cost around 2000Ksh, 21USD.

tank for cooking, drinking, washing, bathing and even laundry. When the rain came, it filled the tank again and again and again, to the point that Mama Margret shared the water with a neighbor who was still in the waiting list to get a tank: *Mimi kuja kukopa baadhi ya maji kutoka kwenu* "I'm coming to borrow some water from you!" Mama Molongo says, *Huwezi kukopa maji kutoka kwangu. hii pia ni maji yako. Huwezi kukopa kilicho chako* "You don't borrow water from me. This is also your water. You don't borrow what is yours," Mama Margret responded. During the dry season, the family would only harvest water from the tank for drinking and cooking. Mama Margret and her daughter Marci would keep fetching water at the Umba River for washing, but the time they spend fetching water at the river had been cut in half.

"Before I had the water tank, during the dry season I had to sell my goats or my cow. Our goats and cows are our bank account around here so it's important for us to keep them and don't sell them. During the dry season it was very hard for us to keep the goats and the cows because we had no food for us and no crops for the animals to eat, so we sold them to get money to purchase some crops for ourselves that would last the whole dry season. You see, it was not an investment, it was just survival. With the water tank, we drink and cook with clean water and we leave the water from the Umba River to give to the animals and to water our *chambas* that give us food to eat. So now when we sell the cow or the goats it's not to eat ourselves but to invest in our children's education since we can pay the fees for their school."

Mama Margret related her owning a water tank to her daughters going to school. However, the tank also meant more reliable meals for the family, more consistent hygiene for all, and also more freedom for her. Mama Margret completed her Train the Trainers program in 2011 and she had more time to talk to the neighbors, hold "health parties" in her community, brainstorm with community leaders, and think about issues that would have been unthinkable for her in the past: she even started playing soccer! Mama Margret belonged to the N-HbM Female Soccer League created at the petition of the women from Jirani; she played for the Godo Team. In addition, in 2013 Mama Margret felt empowered enough to go to the government clinic and request training as a community health worker. As a community health worker for the government and as a health promoter for N-HbM, Mama Margret had to closely monitor every single health indicator and wellbeing factor that affected 20 families of her villages. Every month she would need to fill out paperwork (Mama Margret was illiterate in 2010) describing any change in the health of the families she had to monitor: malaria cases, new births, deaths, any other diseases, etc.

The fight against the lack of water is far from over, though. Several times during the year, I would ask community leaders about the drilling of a water well or the construction of a sand dam that would involve the whole community and in turn assist a broader number of people. I would also talk to the women to share my ideas about water and listen to their insights. Consistently, the leaders and the women have maintained their position saying that they prefer the rainwater tanks because they fear that nobody would take good care of a communal water well or a sand dam. In the future, they claim, "It'd be really good to have a well or other water sources, but not for now." Some women are afraid that communal water well would bring more problems than solutions. Many of the women in the villages have discovered a strong sense of sorority through the N-HbM programs, and they are afraid of doing something to break that alliance.

Mama Damaris Munini "harvesting water"-as the women say- from a
newly installed water tank. Photo by Liliane Calfee.

### *Tailoring School*

Some of the problems that women face in the villages cannot be solved by health education, health services, water or
sanitation. Although all of that helped to improve their quality of
life, the women realized that their cycle of poverty would not be
broken that easily. Again, by listening to the women I heard that
they wanted a fair chance to live from their own labor. They had
understood the meaning of wellbeing and wanted to be more than
objects and subjects of health education and health services; they
wanted to be active agents of their health and wellbeing! They
were talking about raising poultry and selling eggs, getting more
goats, boosting the small vegetable businesses to sell at the local
market, buying sewing machines. In 2010 Mama Damaris, a single
mother of two young daughters was the first one to suggest getting

a sewing machine. The Tailoring School for girls and women was about to be born.

"Why aren't you greeting Mama Damaris?" Mama Bendettah scolded me, surprised by my insolent manners. That was in 2011, two days after I arrived in Lunga Lunga. Apparently Mama Damaris was in front of me, smiling at me, but I swore I did not see her. In front of me there was an attractive young woman wearing a pretty wig and dressed in a stunning green and blue flower outfit; large green earrings and a scarf around her head matched the dress and gave her the most dignified demeanor. Again, in my unconscious mind I had already internalized that women in "that part of Africa" do not dress well, do not have time to care about themselves, and in fact do not care about their appearance. With the sewing machine provided to Mama Damaris in 2010, she had managed to create her own business as a dressmaker and generate an income that gave her enough not only to merely survive, but also to send her two daughters to school, make her own clothes and take good care of her own appearance, as she claimed she had always wanted.

Mama Damaris and Mama Bendettah, both of them former fruit sellers in the market and now leaders in Lunga Lunga, suggested buying more sewing machines and giving the chance to other women to do what she had done.

In three years, there were more than twenty sewing machines and around one hundred women and girls trained in the tailoring industry and examined by the government with the tailoring national examination that permitted them to open a private business and use their skills to make clothes to sell, even school uniforms, and build their livelihoods. Mr. Athuman, the local teacher from Perani, trained since then all sorts of girls, primarily teenage mothers and school dropouts. Furthermore, one of the goals of the tailoring school was to prevent the trafficking of girls for sexual exploitation. Given the strategic location of Lunga

Lunga and other villages around the border with Tanzania, hundreds of trucks fill the road that crosses town—the Mombasa Rd. It is well known in the villages that girls are often abducted, or allured to work in the sex industry in Mombasa, Nairobi, Kampala or other cities of neighboring countries. Lack of work in the rural areas makes the girls want to go to the city where they are easy prey for the growing sex industry. The tailoring school keeps them busy and gives them skills to join the workforce and make a living for themselves. The school is not completely free of charge: the girls pay a symbolic fee that makes them commit to persevere with their classes. Although the fee is symbolic, all fees together help pay the teacher's salary.

Tailoring students practicing their skills before examination for their official government certificate. Photo by Liliane Calfee.

The *Nikumbuke* Tailoring School became global when the University of Wisconsin-Madison conceived the Wisconsin

Without Borders Marketplace (WWBM) that would sell bags and dresses made by the women in Lunga Lunga to return the profit to the women and keep the cycle of sewing moving forward.

### *Moringa Tree Sustainability Project*

The Moringa Tree Sustainability Project was the culmination of women's work towards peace and wellbeing. It was as if the women knew the four core values of the Green Belt Movement created by Kenyan activist and ecofeminist Wangari Maathai (Maathai 2010, 14-15): love for the environment, gratitude and respect for the Earth's resources; self-empowerment and self-betterment; and a spirit of service and volunteerism. But the women in the villages went far beyond these core values. There was not only love for the environment and altruism, it was also the desire to create sustainable income-generating activities and increase the supply of iron in the diet so that pregnant women who craved iron did not have to masticate pieces of mud to satiate their craving. This collaborative effort empowered women to work symbiotically with the environment in order to foster community health and togetherness.

Nikumbuke-HbM had been born within the context of an ever-degrading natural environment, and of fewer trees and increasingly sandy landscapes. While the water tanks were able to provide drinking water for the communities, they were not addressing the root cause of local water loss. When the Moringa project was proposed, the women deeply understood that those trees would provide both direct and indirect health benefits—direct through the consumption of leaves, indirect through the improvement of the water, air, and soil quality in the surrounding areas. For these reasons, the women were eager to participate in a tree-planting project. Women, after all, were the ones who worked as agriculturalists day in and day out growing the food that would feed their families. Furthermore, some of the women came to the conclusion that planting the Moringa tree would allow them to save money in indirect ways, for example by going to the doctor less. Other women had plans to sell the leaves in the market and make some profit out of the project. From the beginning, though, it was clear that the women did not understand this project as only the commodification of nature, and that selling the leaves was a small part of this comprehensive project.

For N-HbM, the planting of Moringa trees aimed at enhancing and cementing the achievements of the existing programs by combating food insecurity—poverty, illness and mal/undernutrition, especially for pregnant women and adolescent girls.[29]—and deforestation The goal was to plant around seven hundred Moringa trees—one hundred trees in the environs of each village.[30] The direct objectives were to improve the local diet and health—particularly for women and children—, and reforesting the area.[31] The indirect objectives were to foster women's leaderships and control of their own lives through the creation of a Moringa Cooperative, and contributing to quality of life and general wellbeing of the communities.

Lunga Lunga and the six surrounding villages were—and continue to be—a prime location for Moringa Oleifera cultivation. Not only was the tree naturalized in the area, but also the semi-arid land was perfect for Moringa growth. Given the reported health problems in the area and the fact that desertification was increasingly an environmental and community health risk (FAO,

[29] The extensive list of vitamins and minerals is very important for pregnant women. The vitamins from crushed dried Moringa Oleifera leaves or powder include, but are not limited to: A, B1, B2, B3, and E; fresh leaves are full of vitamin C—far more than the amount of vitamin C found in orange juice; dried leaves contain an impressive amount of minerals like magnesium, copper, phosphorus, and zinc.
[30] Perani, Mpakani, Godo, Jirani, Umoja, and Maasailand.
[31] The Moringa Oleifera tree species is very well suited for this region since it is autochthonous from Kenya and thrives in dry environments that are largely inhospitable to other plant species.

1992), planting the Moringa trees within N-HbM's general programs framework seemed like a good fit for all. The health benefits of the Moringa Oleifera tree, particularly for women and children, are extensive. It combats malnutrition, increases the birth weight of newborns, enhances breast milk production in nursing mothers, and aids in childbirth recovery (Estrella and others, 2000; Marcu, 2013). Besides, the use of the Moringa tree also gives back to the environment, representing the symbiotic relationship with nature by growing best in dry areas, allowing the absorption of water from the subsoil with its long taproot, holding down groundwater, and improving soil quality for surrounding crops (Ndubuaka and others, 2014).

During the first phase of the project, community women were trained as peer-educators in order to lead their own education campaigns to gain community interest in the health and economic advantages of the Moringa tree. The planting and harvesting of hundreds of Moringa trees motivated women into becoming leaders of their own green movement. In addition, the launching of the Moringa Tree Cooperative increased women's income through job creation and income generating activities, which in turn enhanced women's status and provided an opportunity for self-empowerment and development in their own terms.

According to the N-HbM team, the Moringa Oleifera tree became an exceptional plant to work with, for it was a living example of the human potential to work symbiotically with nature. The first trees planted around the Community Health Center grew wild; roughly around 15 feet tall without being pruned. To show the women how the trees sprouted, the leaders halved one of the trees, and within two weeks the tree had sprouted about eight new limbs to compensate for the amount removed. The women were able to produce a substantial amount of powder from the leaves while simultaneously encouraging the tree to grow.

The use of a Moringa mill also constituted an appropriate use of technology that served to promote natural balance. As mentioned before, properly pruning the tree provided large quantities of powder, but making powder took time that the already busy women simply did not have. The mill machine became a way for women to still engage with nature and with the Moringa trees without having to drastically alter their daily schedules. The Cooperative also was a space where women could gather and work on a common task. Indeed, it has become an object of pride for the women and has come to symbolize community collaboration and the success that the women have had together.

The importance of involving women as leaders of the Moringa project could not be underestimated. Kwale County women work long hours in the fields, providing sustenance for their families while simultaneously living as second-class citizens and their work undervalued. As a result, they are often not recognized as real farmers and subsequently receive no formal training or advisory services within development projects (van Vank 2013). At N-HbM, the inclusion and empowerment of women in this project was seen as pivotal to the health of the entire community. Madam Bendettah put it this way[32]:

"You find back at their homes, the director of the food [and] of managing the home is the woman. So if we had to teach the men, I don't think it will be 100%. Because many they have many other things doing outside their homes. But you find with the women, they want to try. Every woman wants her family to look healthy, so they will try their level best. And most of the time they are with their families. And they know, because you'll find in Africa if the kids or any member of the family is sick, it is the work

[32] These interviews were collected in August 2014 by graduate student Erin Campeau during her internship with N-HbM to monitor the Moringa tree project. The English grammar of the interviews has not been altered to make sure that each woman was using her own voice.

of the woman to care for that."

A village elder of Lunga Lunga echoed those words:

"To involve the woman in community is very well because a woman itself is like a whole house... Your husband is there, your children is there, your grandmother, grandfather... the family. A woman is a family. So that is [why] I can say to teach or to introduce women in a community... when you teach a woman, you teach the whole family."

Another woman mentioned:

"If you empower a woman, you empower the whole community. Yes, the whole community will benefit from one mama, you see? And how about if we are many, like this? Don't you think they are empowering one another within the community?"

Involving women in the Moringa Project, indeed delegating them as leaders in their communities, was essential to the success of the entire operation. This meant that by empowering the women, the community at large benefited. It also meant that the recognition of women had the potential to foster wellbeing for all.

The women owned the land on which the mill was located, and the women managed the planting of the trees as well as the effective functioning of the cooperative. The fact that the women hired men as caretakers of the cooperative building constituted a huge shift in power dynamics in the area, and became a large and tangible move toward equal representation. This shift did not suggest a reversal of power dynamics; it was not about women gaining control or taking over the space that men had historically occupied in the area. That women were hiring men did not imply that women were going to maintain power in the communities. Rather, it meant that women were being more equally respected and represented—not more represented, but also not less—in positions that had typically been reserved for men. Because the entire community started benefiting from the project, the women were gaining prestige. Their voices started being heard. Other communities around the area requested the creation of more cooperatives based on the benefits they were seeing for the entire community.

The women who run the cooperative benefited because they were able to charge other members of the community for grinding maize and Moringa. This allowed them to fully own the mill, save for its maintenance, and take the entire project into their own hands. In addition, they did not pay for their own grinding and were thus able to save money. At the same time, the mill provided for the community at large. Prior to the Moringa project, individuals were paying relatively large sums of money in order to travel to faraway corn mills. With this cooperative, they were able to spend less time and less money on transit while simultaneously giving back to their own communities.

Following are some of the answers that the women provided related to the Moringa project. Some of the women focused on the health benefits of the Moringa tree, commenting, too, on its water-purifying qualities and the ways in which it was already impacting personal and community wellbeing:

"For me, when I started using the Moringa... we planted last year. Me, I used to be when I wake up in the morning feeling as if I had worked a lot, but when I started eating Moringa—me I have not used the dried ones, I use the fresh ones. I prepare my cabbages with the leaves, so me, I started... when I wake up in the morning, I don't feel what I was feeling. I also eat the seeds. I prepare about... I eat them. So, me, I say Moringa Tree has done a lot in my body... and my family, too. It (Moringa) is very much helpful in our community. Like now, those who planted earlier, they have helped people with diabetes, with high blood pressure. Those who do use it continuously they don't go to hospital because the immune is strong. When the water is dirty, they can use the seeds to clear the water, so it is helping the community very much."

Madam Bendettah went further, understanding the Moringa tree as a tool for women and community empowerment:

"Yes, with this one since now each and everyone is going to plant this one, we'll see our empowerment will have an [impact] on soils because the leaves we have seen and the rest of the Moringa parts, if you just spread them on top of the soil, the soil will be fertile... We will have fresh oxygen because many trees will be found within our community, and the same thing – you'll find many women, or most of the people living in our community, they will have less diseases. So we'll not have any diseases that can be spread to each other. It will be limited."

She continued by reiterating the ways in which the Moringa tree would benefit the community as a whole by empowering the land that the people shared.

"Yes, with this one you'll find—with empowerment—you know... some places whereby the trees are being cut... you'll find it is a desert somehow or people they are not harvesting anything. Now having this Moringa Project—because we are trying to reach each and every person—and especially whereby it is dry areas whereby they have cut trees, now they are going to plant fresh new trees. Those trees will be bringing oxygen whereby humans they do breathe in. So it will change their empowerment in a way. And you'll find now people they cannot burn these trees because they are not good in charcoal. So you'll find we have no carbon monoxide coming to our people or our animals that they can breathe in."

It was clear that, together, the women had reached an understanding and appreciation of the role that the Moringa project would play in each of the seven communities.

Moringa tree plantation in Lunga Lunga. Photo by HbM Team.

As part of N-HbM's framework, the Moringa project provided a problem-solving space that subsequently contributed to
increased communication and interconnectedness among
community members. Women who had previously had little
contact with each other were working together on a common task:
planting trees for environmental, personal, and community
wellbeing. This interaction and the existence of a shared objective,
values and activities created a group consciousness and social
identification, what Lederach (2005) refers as to minimizing the
tendency to dehumanize the "Other". Spending time together

through the shared task of tree planting, the seven communities created a space that recognized that our quality of life is dependent on the quality of life of others.

Simply stated, the Moringa Cooperative has become a source of community pride, particularly for the women whose voices have been raised throughout the process of its creation. The cooperative has also been an income generating activity that allows community members to sustain themselves in their own way. The Cooperative has never been about the accumulation of capital wealth for any single individual. It was not based upon competition but rather on meeting community needs and wants.

### Community Library and Mini-Free Library: Spreading the Word

In the summer of 2013, a one-room library was built on the grounds of *Nikumbuke* Community Health Center with the intention to provide reading materials to women, men and children from the seven villages. For two main reasons, this would become a very challenging and audacious task. On the one hand, most of the books we had, donated by people from Europe and the United States, were based on a model that only reflected western worldviews, very far from the lifestyle of people in the villages. On the other hand, the majority of people in Kwale County was not literate and would not be able to read either western or non-western materials; we knew that we would have to enhance our imagination to compensate for the challenges.

"If you don't have it, you invent it!" Those were the words of my mother that resonated in my brain. And that is exactly what we did; we invented books! The women and the UW team made-up stories illustrated with drawings that depicted local health concerns and global solutions, producing reading materials where there were none. The lack of printed resources gave us the freedom to conceive and give birth to an extraordinary collection of hand painted recycled cardboard books,[33] with very few and simple words written in both languages Kiswahili and English, but with many illustrations that addressed issues like "what to do when cholera strikes; how to build a latrine; how to clean children's teeth; or how to eat a balanced diet." The UW team along with local girls and women painted hundreds of cardboard covers, some with simple colorful brushstrokes and others with the most sophisticated African figures, symbols and landscapes. For ideas on the inside illustrations, we turned to Hesperian Foundation books, the Internet, and to our own creativity.

Opening this library would give us the unintended opportunity to document the theater dramas of the *Afya Ukumby* that the women had been performing for several years. Since most women actors had no formal education, they created their health dramas orally, kept the scripts in their memory and acted them out over and over again without leaving any written record. The UW team transcribed most of the *Afya Ukumby* dramas and published them with the collaboration of *Kutsemba Cartao* (see note 1).

Although creating a culturally sensitive collection of printed materials seemed an appropriate step forward, it was not enough to honor the traditional and rich oral culture of the many tribes of Kenya, so we decided to publish dozens of oral stories that one year before, in the summer of 2012, one of my students had collected in the villages. This student recorded stories told by women from different ethnic groups. The stories were told and recorded in Kiswahili, transcribed, and translated into English.

---

[33] Through collaboration with *Kutsemba Cartao*, http://kutsembacartao. wix.com/kutsemba the first *Cartonera*, Cardboard Book Publishing, created in Africa, in Mozambique, by UW-Madison Professors Luís Madureira and Saylín Alvárez. Thanks to *Kutsemba Cartao*, we learned how to create cardboard covers, how to print the stories, how to ensemble the books, and everything else we needed to fill the *Nikumbuke* Library with several hundred books.

Titles like "The Frog and the Millipede," "The Path of a Liar is Short," "The Toad's Ambition," "Selfish Woman," "The Rabbit and the Giraffe," and "Why the Ostrich has no Neck Feathers," among others were published through *Kutsemba Cartao* in both English and Kiswahili, with the name and the picture of the woman who had told the story, as the author of the book. This very simple strategy generated a synergy and a ripple effect among those who wanted to tell, those who wanted to write, those who wanted to read and those who wanted to be read.

The *Nikumbuke* Library did not function like a western library in the sense that the books could not be checked out by people; simply, there were not enough books to lend and no personnel to control a borrowing system. The library, however, became an alive and dynamic space, always changing; people read books but also wrote books, people removed books but also created books. Children scribbled over existing drawings but they also illustrated new books. The people of the seven villages were the ones who gave life to this library, creating and recreating its content, giving it an identity of its own, and using the library in a way that fitted their needs and wants.

One year after the opening of the *Nikumbuke Library*, we built a Little Free Library[34] (literally a small wooden box supported by a pole stuck in the ground) that could be used twenty-four hours a day and the seven days of the week. The purpose of this wooden box was very different from the original idea of the Little Free Libraries created in the United States, whose motto "Take a book, Return a Book" would not work in this part of the

[34] The first Little Free Library was built in 2009 by Todd Bol in Hudson, Wisconsin. In 2012, the Little Free Library became a nonprofit organization. The main idea of the libraries was "take a book, leave a book," becoming a tool for book exchange and free knowledge sharing. The libraries became a global sensation and as per 2018 there are more than 60,000 libraries, present in all 50 of the United States and over 80 countries; millions of books are exchanged each year.

world. The purpose of this particular Little Free Library was for Nurse Josephine and for Madam Bendettah to leave pamphlets, flyers and small handmade books containing important health messages for the community that the people could freely get to share with their families and neighbors.

Mini-Free Library installed at the *Nikumbuke* Community Health Center in Lunga Lunga. Photo by HbM Team.

### *Female Soccer League*

Competence as rivalry and cooperation are two sides of the same coin. Competence as "competency" also means possibilities or human capacities that can be interpreted as "powers" whereby women have been able to recover the notion of capacity or capability, and empowerment.[35]

The women from Jirani took the initiative. They were the ones who were pioneers as agents of their own mental and physical health. "What is next for Jirani?" I asked them one year. "What do we want to achieve for next year in Jirani?" The women did not speak; they were looking at each other as if they had something to say but did not want to dare. Suddenly one of them raised her hand and shouted, *We want a soccer team!! Light Blue!* the women shouted, already selecting their color.

The day of the first soccer game between Jirani and Mpakani women was one of the most unique moments we had witnessed in the area. The women from the two villages had been practicing for several months every single day. How can women in remote and impoverished villages practice every day? Well... N-HbM had supplied women with rain water tanks and many of the women who used to spend a minimum of 9 hours a day fetching water could use that precious time to practice soccer or do whatever they wanted or needed with their time because they did not have to fetch water for many months.

Jirani won! The women from the two villages played to the death, like gladiators on the arena. Hundreds and hundreds of spectators gathered to see this unique event. During each break, some of the women players breastfed their babies who were waiting with relatives. The Maasai villages said *We want another soccer team!* Perani women shouted *We are next!* Lunga Lunga claimed *No, no, we are next! Next year we'll compete!* All the women wanted to play. The spectators commented that they never had so much fun in their lives. All ethnic groups united, all tribes united. The games were not tribe against tribe but village against

---

[35] Based on the 16th century etymological meaning as *compete*, and added the 17th century Latin meaning as *competentia*—meeting together, agreement, come together; https://www.etymonline.com/word/competence

village, since several ethnic groups and tribes compose each village.

The dream of forming a Female Soccer League in Kwale County became a reality in 2015 when one of my former undergraduate students obtained a grant to fund the equipment for all seven villages. The seven villages formed their teams according to their own criteria. The result was a mostly even representation of tribes and ages of players, many of whom were grandmothers. The teams selected their colors and practiced tirelessly for six months, every single day of the week. In May 2015, three members of N-HbM from the United States went to Lunga Lunga to witness the anticipated kick-off of the League. If the first match of 2014 had been the most unique experience we had witnessed in the area, this competition was without a doubt the most magical event that we experienced during all those years in Kwale County.

The opening ceremony started with two prayers—a Muslim prayer and a Christian prayer. With these prayers, the women embodied the fact that differences do not need to be erased and that diverse beliefs can and must be respected. The teams were well formed and impeccably uniformed, with their *kangas* on top covering the short pants until the game started; all the women uncover their *kangas* at the same time. They all formed a large line by teams and greeted the several hundred spectators. The games began and each and every single woman left her skin, soul and heart in what resembled a battlefield more than a soccer playground. It was obvious which team had had the most proper coaching and training. The Maasai women, who had never ever dreamed of playing soccer, capitalized all their energy and dominated the ball as if they had been playing for ages.

In all cases, the referee was a man from Lunga Lunga. Every time a goal was scored, the women spectators from that village crowded in the field, running and clapping, dancing and singing to cheer their team. The women from the seven villages spent the whole endless day playing the Tournament, for semi-finals and also for finals. So much was expected that day, so much was fulfilled that day. Jirani and Mpakani made it to the final round; Jirani won the Tournament.

The women kept practicing after the Tournament, with less intensity than before, but they developed more resistance and more aptitudes as players.

Female soccer teams from Jirani and Mpakani, the first two communities that competed together. Photo by Ali Miller.

## Our Model for Collaboration: A Summary

The work of N-HbM is multidisciplinary in essence but most importantly it is interdisciplinary, taking advantage of the interpellation and contestation of multiple disciplines—public health, gender studies and feminisms, medical anthropology, history, philosophy, and peace studies among others. Because no one single discipline, or even the combination of them, can tell the whole story, this interdisciplinary approach has allowed us to challenge different disciplines in their work towards gender equality, sustainable health and women's wellbeing.

The structural model that N-HbM has used for the organization and implementation of its programs is circular in nature, starting with the women and finishing with the women—with their desires, needs, wants, and concerns. Another stage of the circular model involves the local government and the Ministry of Health, getting their approval, permission and support. An additional step in the model entails the transformation of academic research and knowledge into the appropriate cultural setting of rural Kenya. The last phase consists of getting the women's feedback on the proposed programs, again according to the women's desires, needs, wants, and concerns; and the cyclic model starts over again.

Very early during the first stage of the circular model, the women showed their strength, their capacity, their abilities, not only to learn but also to act upon what they were learning. In other words, and as Martha C. Nussbaum puts it in her work on women and development (2000), the women found their own capabilities maximizing their competencies and feeling revalued. In this sense, the power—or empowerment—, that women showed was not something given by "us" as external agents from the University of Wisconsin-Madison; power was something that was recovered, reconstructed from their own possibilities. We could say that the women discovered their own empowerment and regained control of their lives because they encountered the right circumstances and the adequate structures at the right time for them. During the process of control regaining, some of the women talked about "others controlling their lives," while some others talked about themselves feeling "out of control." In the first group of women, the control came from structures of power that maintained the status quo perpetuating structural violence. In the second group, the lack of control seemed to emerge from the "self." Regardless of the source of disempowerment, the women wanted to feel in control of their lives, which is an interpretation of empowerment. As mediators, the programs of N-HbM facilitated the revalorization or empowerment with the following in mind:

1. Clarification of what we, N-HbM and the women, wanted to achieve.

2. Clarification of the options and possibilities of both N-HbM and of the women.

3. Acknowledgment of the different types of knowledge and ways of knowing that all parties could provide.

4. Enhancement of the abilities of all parts involved in order to transform knowledges using the capacities of listening, communicating, organizing, analyzing themes and evaluating alternatives.

5. Recognition and acknowledgment of the diverse resources to achieve what the women wanted and the fulfillment of N-HbM objectives.

6. Reinforcement of women's capacity to take action, not only thinking about the end result but also about the paths to follow during the process of knowledge acquisition.

In order to re-encounter women's inner power, or to recover their suppressed empowerment, N-HbM took a participatory approach and a conceptual framework based on "performative theory" that acknowledges that humans can form, perform, reform and reshape human relations (with our bodies, with our environment, with each other, with ourselves) in different ways, and of course, using not only knowledge, but also care, tenderness, kindness, compassion, empathy and love in a way that we can transform the distribution of resources to avoid exclusion and misery, and create new projects and programs that align with gender equality, politics of health, sustainable development and peace.

HbAM as depicted in the graphic model below, was implemented in the context of a partnership and supportive network that included Universities, NGOs, communities, and government agencies. This model depicts the array of activities, strategies, philosophical principles and partners that came together in the HbAM. At the center and heart of the model is "feminist emotion," defined as effective and emotional practices related to experiencing gender in patriarchal contexts. Part II will explore this concept in great detail, and reveal it to be a key aspect of possible extension with context-specific adaptation of the HbAM model.

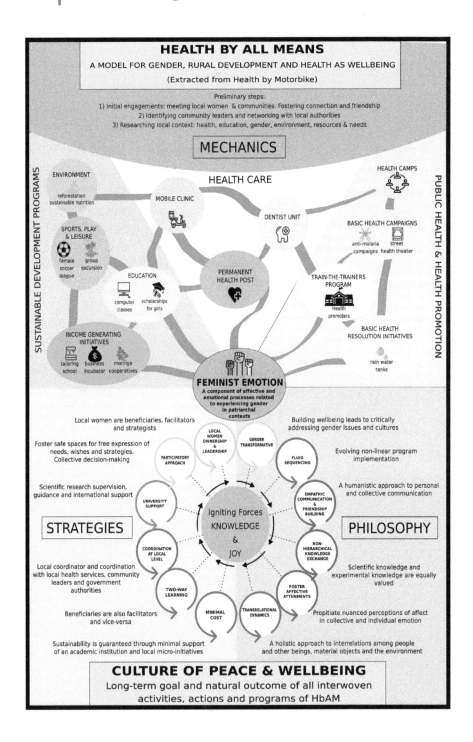

# HEALTH BY ALL MEANS

A MODEL FOR GENDER, RURAL DEVELOPMENT AND HEALTH AS WELLBEING

(Extracted from Health by Motorbike)

Preliminary steps:
1) Initial engagements: meeting local women & communities. Fostering connection and friendship
2) Identifying community leaders and networking with local authorities
3) Researching local context: health, education, gender, environment, resources & needs

## MECHANICS

HEALTH CARE

SUSTAINABLE DEVELOPMENT PROGRAMS

PUBLIC HEALTH & HEALTH PROMOTION

ENVIRONMENT
reforestation
sustainable nutrition

MOBILE CLINIC

HEALTH CAMPS

DENTIST UNIT

BASIC HEALTH CAMPAIGNS
anti-malaria    street
campaigns  health theater

SPORTS, PLAY
& LEISURE
female    group
soccer   excursion
league

EDUCATION
computer   scholarships
classes    for girls

PERMANENT
HEALTH POST

TRAIN-THE-TRAINERS
PROGRAM
Health
promoters

INCOME GENERATING
INITIATIVES
tailoring  business  moringa
school   incubator cooperatives

BASIC HEALTH
RESOLUTION INITIATIVES

rain water
tanks

FEMINIST EMOTION
A component of affective and
emotional processes related
to experiencing gender
in patriarchal
contexts

Local women are beneficiaries, facilitators
and strategists

Building wellbeing leads to critically
addressing gender issues and cultures

Foster safe spaces for free expression of
needs, wishes and strategies.
Collective decision-making

LOCAL
WOMEN
OWNERSHIP
&
LEADERSHIP

GENDER
TRANSFORMATIVE

PARTICIPATORY
APPROACH

FLUID
SEQUENCING

Evolving non-linear program
implementation

Scientific research supervision,
guidance and international support

UNIVERSITY
SUPPORT

EMPATHIC
COMMUNICATION
&
FRIENDSHIP
BUILDING

A humanistic approach to personal
and collective communication

## STRATEGIES

Igniting Forces
KNOWLEDGE
&
JOY

## PHILOSOPHY

COORDINATION
AT LOCAL
LEVEL

NON-
HIERARCHICAL
KNOWLEDGE
EXCHANGE

Local coordinator and coordination
with local health services, community
leaders and government
authorities

TWO-WAY
LEARNING

FOSTER
AFFECTIVE
ATTUNMENTS

Scientific knowledge and
experimental knowledge are equally
valued

Beneficiaries are also facilitators
and vice-versa

MINIMAL
COST

TRANSRELATIONAL
DYNAMICS

Propitiate nuanced perceptions of affect
in collective and individual emotion

Sustainability is guaranteed through minimal support
of an academic institution and local micro-initiatives

A holistic approach to interrelations among people
and other beings, material objects and the environment

# CULTURE OF PEACE & WELLBEING
Long-term goal and natural outcome of all interwoven
activities, actions and programs of HbAM

PART II

PHILOSOPHY AND THEORY

Teresa Langle de Paz

## Background

Once upon a morning I was reading the newspaper at my house in the northern part of Madrid, Spain. After one hour scanning through very discouraging international and national political news, I got to a back-cover article entitled *"Déjame contarte un cuento"* (*Let Me Tell You a Story*). The reporter, Pilar Álvarez, was writing from Doha, Qatar. The article narrated the successful story of Rana Dajani, a native of Jordan and a professor of Molecular Biology at the University of Iowa. She has created a program for four-to-twelve year old Jordanian children called *We Love Reading*, run by seven hundred volunteers. Just by listening to stories being read to them and posted at a Virtual Library, a large number of children—up to ten thousand—had significantly improved their learning skills and outcomes at school. Although the educational impacts are important, I was more interested in learning about how the volunteer women had become empowered by their experiences as volunteers in this program. They had learned to speak in public, and enhanced their self-confidence to the point that some of them had even opened their own businesses.

When I heard Araceli Alonso share her experiences in Kenya in a lecture entitled: "The Great Power of Small Ideas," I was struck by the same dynamic of simplicity and transformation. "It is so easy to change the world," Ara said, "Why can't people see it?" Her question echoed the words of Rana Dajani: "If you wish to foster change, think of something small and focus on doing it as well as possible." [36]

I could not stop thinking that the success stories of *We Love Reading* in Jordan and *Nikumbuke-Health by Motorbike* (N-

---

[36] Original words: "Si quieres conseguir un cambio, piensa en algo pequeño y simple y concéntrate en hacerlo lo mejor posible."

HbM) in Kenya, had something very important in common: With very low resources and an approach focused on the *micro* they promoted wide-ranging and deeply transformative programs. Both programs gave opportunities to people, children and adult women, to express themselves freely and safely, and to expand their creative imagination and other capacities; both initiatives also fostered joy and instigated heartfelt communication. The outcome spanned beyond planned expectations and foreseen results. In Jordan, listening to stories helps children to improve skills at school; but through the process of voluntary storytelling, the program also became a women's empowerment resource. As Araceli Alonso evokes, in Kenya the process by which women told their stories and recalled their lived experiences, triggered in them a thirst for knowledge that was very empowering for them and resulted in highly productive gender awareness and advocacy initiatives.

So many important unexpected outcomes that sprouted out of N-HbM programs. Theater united ethnic enemies as well as men and women. Tree planting motivated Christians and Muslims to work together for a common cause. The opportunity to see the ocean and play together broke gender hierarchies, and millenary cultural prejudices were temporarily neutralized. Joy overcame pain and poverty through a soccer league. Women became respected community health leaders and saved the lives of many. Water tank installations sent girls to school and fostered communal collaborative spirit.

How was change nurtured, multiplied, expanded in Lunga Lunga? The lived experiences told to me by Ara resonated deeply with rough the theoretical framework that I have developed around affect and gender, called *feminist emotion*. This impulse promotes affective exchanges and enhances positive affect, building peace through social change. The present and the future are built upon these roots which can grow to foster collaboration, expanding human capacities, creating spaces where women can get to know each other and learn of each other's vulnerabilities, I will undertake a close examination of N-HbM programs to illustrate how setting affect in motion and fostering women's attunements to their primary forms of agency in gendered affect, can allow affect and emotions to become an unstoppable force for social harmony, joy and peace.[37]

A departing assumption of my analysis of the programs in Kenya is that a gender, health and development model may be extracted from the happenings in a particular region of Kenya where the N-HbM initiative was promoted over the last few years, and that such model exists prior to interpretation. However, it is through interpretation that its elusiveness, the living material of human experience and the ambivalence of its meaning, may be turned into replicable action. The N-HbM programs are the means for the materialization of survival of many women of the geographical area where they operate but also of the possibility for a "better life." In turn, such materialization manifests through sparks of a shared feeling of having a "better life" which have become the venue through which the programs are shaped into concrete actions. The very basic need to keep living must be covered first: Health. But health is not the absence of disease; health is life, hope, and a venue to wellbeing and peace. This is how the *Health by All Means* model (HbAM) was born: Health became something else beyond staying alive.

The happenings described and explained in Part I of this book should be scrutinized as potentially replicable, with adaptation anywhere. I propose an interpretation based on a feminist examination of how setting affect in motion and fostering certain

---

[37] For more information on my theoretical stand you may consult my most recent monographic book published in Spanish: *La urgencia de vivir. Teoría feminista de las emociones* (Barcelona: Anthropos, 2018) or a recent essay in English: "A Golden Lever for Politics: Feminist Emotion and Women's Agency" (*Hypatia. A Journal of Feminist Philosophy*. 2016. 31(2): 187-203.

emotional processes and women's attunements to them through several programs and activities, turned into an unstoppable force to build social harmony, joy and peace. Yes, the model existed prior to my interpretation, just like my interpretation was lacking something before I visited Lunga Lunga; just like people always know at some level what they need and what needs to be done before they get the assistance to rationalize it and realize it. Before I saw with my own eyes and felt the warmth of the people on my skin, sensed the force of Nikumbuke women, breathed the hope in the air, my insights about affective and emotional processes fell short of what I was talking about: the affective dimension of reality. I had been trying to intellectually capture affect, but actually affect captured me. It is only now that I have been to Lunga Lunga, now that I have met some of the women that Araceli Alonso has been working with, that I can understand why, in Kiswahili, "Nikumbuke" means "Remember me.

What does it take to theorize about the intricacies of people's interactions with other people and beings, with themselves, and with the environment? One of the main accomplishments of the programs was in fact that such intricacies did not seem to entail many problems or become obstacles in the processes of fostering women's capabilities and in promoting collective work within certain ethical values and a shared emotional ground. I started thinking about these issues in Foucaultian terms and wondered what were the *technologies and the self* and *techniques of the body* that were being fostered so that the women of Lunga Lunga so successfully self-examined themselves and others, reflexively and non-reflexively, and were strongly inclined towards modifying certain *habitus*, skills, identities, values, customary norms (Foucault 1988; Burkitt 2012). What made the Nikumbuke women empowered as women and what type of empowerment was it about that enabled them to so easily question and reverse certain gender *habitus*? The answer to these questions would not be clear cut. Instead, it was going to unfold itself gradually encompassed with the very narrative and narration process of this essay.

I started referring to the N-HbM approach as "humanistic" because it seemed to me that strengthened human connections and collaborations were the soul of the programs and their most relevant outcome however, this appellative was not very convincing. By it I meant that at the core of N-HbM programs was a maximizing effort to boost each person's "functionings" or capabilities; in Amartya Sen's terms, the programs were literally about "human development" (Sen 1999). I had not yet visited Lunga Lunga. There still was a two-fold problem to be conceptually resolved. On the one hand, a better understanding of what happens when connections, collaborations, and personal capabilities are so utterly enhanced; on the other, a more satisfactory argumentation about why the enhancement of connections, collaborations and personal capabilities came along with gender awareness and certain forms of feminist empowerment. A theoretical framework had yet to be pinned down to analyze N-HbM programs and provide some insights.

Nothing can stop change once it starts if it comes from the very source of people's souls and minds; their will for a better life, and heartfelt desire for personal growth, love, solidarity, identification. It is a need for positive human connection that fuels community change. Bendettah Thomas, the local coordinator of N-HbM, knows it well. She told me recently that if funding was cut off, or if she and Josephine Matini—the nurse of the programs—stopped working in Lunga Lunga, changes will still spread and germinate through the Nikumbuke women's willingness to go on. What she was really saying is that there is no way back.

## The Situation Upon Arrival

As the plane crossed the Mediterranean towards the African continent, Europe was diluted like an irrelevant domain that, ironically, happened to be my safe personal universe. The new set of emotions and sensations that overtook me were going to stay for many days, and replaced the preeminent role that my intellectual reasoning and imagination had up to this point. As time became slower, stretched and somehow suspended by the slow train that took us from Nairobi to Mombasa through Maasai Mara National wildlife refuge after our flight, I was turned into an insignificant stranger, heavily and helplessly moving into the magnificent night of my mind. We must surrender to this moment. A shifting and twisting pace lead me to meaning thanks to a sense of me that was not mine anymore. A previously imagined scenario will always fall short. Imagination fails us inevitably. The exhausting journey simply took over and brought me to an envisioned place that was, ultimately, completely unexpected. The sounds of the night, the motion of the train and the heat predicted my nakedness, the futility of my mind I was to be confronted with upon arrival.

The intricacies of life could only be glimpsed through emotions and sensations. I had an instinctive resistance to surrendering. I pretended that imagined meaning, intellectually constructed anticipations of the different stages of the journey were with me on the train compartment; one more passenger, like us, into the night. I had no choice but to accept that it was me, a stranger to myself, who was sitting by my side. I tried to cling to my mind skepticism to avoid an additional realization: although Araceli Alonso had taken this trip many times before, she was just another fragile shadow of the night train on its way to Mombasa. I could feel how her emotions permeated her thoughts. I tried to imitate how she enjoyed the pleasure of abandoning herself into a pure moment of vulnerability. But the daylight betrayed my repeated attempts. We arrived at Mombasa. I could not help but to simultaneously be myself and the stranger that I had become during the journey. I did not know by then that I was going to desperately hold on to my imagination and intellectual knowledge of what I had previously extracted from several conversations, readings, and meetings with several people about N-HbM. However, fortunately, I was forced by affect to consider the stranger in me and surrender to this realization.

Let me now examine what, in my view, happened, through a theoretical framework of *feminist emotion*, as the N-HbM programs rather organically developed into specific actions.

## Theoretical Framework. *Feminist Emotion*

### *Affect*

As I read Araceli Alonso's ethnographic account and pursued my own research on affect, emotions and feminism, it occurred to me that a naturally or spontaneously flowing utilization of the *affective matter* related to human social existence and experiences had to be part of the operative means and approach to development matters of N-HbM in Lunga Lunga. Yes, emotionality appeared to always be at the center of communication, both for the foreign actors that assisted the local women and for the local women themselves; the women from Lunga Lunga, Perani, Mpakani, Godo, Jirani, Umoja, and Maasailand who belonged to diverse ethnic groups and communities. Affect and emotions as a *modus operandi*, a force not to be eluded, ignored or wasted, was being channeled so skillfully and productively that it prompted a deep positive transformation of the relationships among women, communities, ethnic groups. Here was another key to N-HbM:

The promotion of multi-faceted change towards a general comprehensive goal of addressing gender issues, health, and wellbeing is triggered and fostered through skillful handling of affect.

Actions promoted by N-HbM are based on the productive power of affect as a core principle. The fact that I had been doing extensive research on emotions for years no doubt guided me in coming to such a conclusion as a departing point of my analysis. But—I told myself—it is neither any kind of affect nor just affect at large. Over the years, in my scientific research, I identified an aspect of affect that manifests stealthily as rebelliousness and referred to it as a latent component of affective processes, inextricably linked to gender experiences in patriarchal settings. I call it *feminist emotion*. Affective rebelliousness emerges everywhere and circulates all over; it is provoked by gender unbalance and the experiences of discrimination. As such, *feminist emotion* can be interpreted as a primary form of agency. In my view, there is an undercurrent of *feminist emotion* in the circulating affective forces that lurk in in the empowerment processes of the women in the Lunga Lunga area. My theoretical framework around *feminist emotion*, lays the ground for my analysis of N-HbM programs and approach; it provides a prism through which to better understand and explain the incredible happenings that this book is about.

Elsewhere I have defined *feminist emotion* as follows:

*Feminist emotion* is a primary form of agency that manifest through a wide range of variations and nuances of emotion as rooted at the empirical level of socialization. It is dispersed and fragmented throughout fluctuating affective processes that can be conceptually grasped with the lenses of phenomenology and paying attention to situated processes; it can be practically utilized through mechanisms that set affect in motion in a specific way and context, for instance, the mechanisms described in this manual (Langle de Paz 2016).

*Feminist emotion* derives from lived, historically and circumstantially situated, dimensions of gender as a subjugating condition that restrains women's—or people (self)identified as non-males—opportunities for wellbeing and flourishing, in hegemonic patriarchal power-unbalanced contexts. For women, *feminist emotion* is a sort of agency in its purest affective and non-reasoning form because they are inescapably and intuitively guided by/in affect to not accept, resist or rebel against gender-based oppression and discrimination. Put it differently, multifaceted historically situated gendered experiences unavoidably produce *affective rebelliousness* towards the contextual limitations, the structural violence, and disadvantaged circumstances that, one way or another, shape experiences of non-male gender. As I mentioned above, my very first deduction of the success of N-HbM programs was that an elusive and ambivalent source of an affective nature fueled its smooth operational means. A closer look at the development of the programs and a direct contact with their protagonists and agents was going to be sufficient to assert that a specific type of affective matter, tainted by *feminist emotion*, was also everywhere, precisely as a component of many emotional processes that emerged over the years as a result of N-HbM initiatives.

As women engage with the world and their own circumstances, their existences are deeply touched by gender inequalities through a complex array of interactive factors; the case of Lunga Lunga and nearby villages was no different. But I was seeking to capture the nuanced lived dimensions of such an array. I wanted to better understand how the women who participated in the programs had managed to sort out, endure, rebel against, ignore, and even subvert some gender induced constraints, *right there*, *right then.* My own assumptions and theoretical premises around *feminist emotion* were very useful to begin exploring how the Nikumbuke women, guided by the N-HbM local coordinator and the international facilitators, made use of the incommensurable agency potential that always spins out of an affective encounter with a gendered world. Thus, the point of departure or hypothesis for my analysis was that the success of the N-HbM should be analyzed from a feminist theoretical angle that would allow for relating its humanistic and comprehensive approach to health and wellbeing and its scientifically informed mechanics to a productive and effective utilization of gender induced affect and emotions.

Although the focus of my interpretation of the events in Lunga Lunga is *emotionality*, I am not referring to emotions as traditionally understood (e.g. anger, fear, rage, love, frustration, joy, etc.). I depart from the non-traditional idea that emotions are shaped by numerous constituents of bodily affective responses and are not clear-cut, stable or monolithic, but have a procedural behavior. Historically, numerous feminist theorists have tried to explain what happens at the emotional level to women since and when their lives are in so many ways deeply touched by the gender asymmetries that rule most of the world. Allison Jaggar, for instance, argued for the need to pay attention to what she called "outlaw emotions," emotions that do not support norms and values and thus involve women's critical "epistemic resource" about socialization (Jaggar 1989). As mentioned above, one of the constituents of emotional processes that are triggered by the experiences of gender in a woman's personal, historical and specific living circumstances and context is what I refer to as *rebellious affect.* Such a rebellious constituent of diverse emotional responses may be detected when emotionality is explored in the context of situated gender analysis and when experience is addressed within the framework of a comprehensive and inter-disciplinary strategy to wellbeing. Nevertheless, it is necessary to start from the assumption that it exists; that rebellious affect caused by non-male gendered experiences is inextricable from social existence in patriarchal settings.

Let me reiterate that the term and concept, *feminist emotion* refers to the following phenomenon: Emotional processes, that are part of non-reasoning consciousness, are inevitably linked to the social dimension of human existence, which is, among other things, deeply touched by unbalanced gender power dynamics for women. Postcolonial theory provided some tools to understand the power shifts and abuses that gave rise to the world we are witnessing. Specifically, postcolonial feminist theory opened new windows to better see and understand the situatedness of gender in the context of a historical past of colonization and the economic globalization of the present. In the 1980s, gender mainstreaming was incorporated into the analysis of globalization to shed light onto global realities that were particularly relevant to development studies, such as the feminization of poverty, lack of access to education, informal work markets, gender based violence, sex trafficking, etc. Also, a new vision to resolve the world economic unbalance inherited from colonial times and aggravated by economic globalization was posed first by Amartya Sen and later, by Martha C. Nussbaum with their revolutionary concept of "human development". They referred to the greatest importance of fostering what people "can be"—capabilities—together with promoting venues for people "to have" and "to do"—needs and wants—to amend the world unbalances and promote modernization (Sen 1999; Nussbaum 2000) Such conceptual shifts and scientific venues entailed a no-return break for grassroots development programs.

After almost five decades of major research advancements in development studies and feminist theory, the need to do situated analysis can no longer be avoided or undervalued to understand how so many intersecting factors contribute to shaping people's realities and circumstances and thus, to molding change. The same applies to gender issues that can neither be avoided in international agendas nor as a category of analysis or an isolated factor. I believe that whereas intersectionality makes us aware of the complexities and distinct characteristics of experience, such precision must also be placed side by side to our endless quest for the shared terrains of human existence. This means that a universalizing interpretative twist to gender analysis is also relevant to comprehend what happens in/through emotionality and to add clarity to intersectional approaches. Life is a complicated entanglement of personal joy and drama; a matter of degree, context, circumstances, and dispositions. There is much to say about what constitutes such complexity to describe the affective nuances of a person and a group. Also, there is much to say about the origins and causes of people's harsh living circumstances in different contexts and places, as is the case of Lunga Lunga and surroundings. Philosophically speaking, I believe that it is at the confluence of intersectionality and universality in emotionality that ontology and politics meet. New conceptual prisms to do justice to such convergence must be developed to better understand the tangible bodily dimensions of gender issues in the real-world power dynamics and structural violence.

Traditionally, emotions have been conceived as individual non-rational responses to stimulus. However, much recent scientific research deeply questions that there is a sharp division line between affect and cognition, and that individual affective manifestations are tainted by group dynamics and shaped by context. The focus of attention has shifted from prioritizing the nature of psychological states to analyzing processes and relationality as the root cause of affect and derived emotional processes. In addition, the so-called "affective turn" or interest in the emotional and affective dimension of life that started to permeate diverse spheres of knowledge over two decades ago, is much more than a trend in the social sciences or the humanities. It is a rather revolutionary way of thinking about the rationally ungraspable dimensions of a rapidly changing world.[38] These scientific trends surely open exciting possibilities for us to reflect upon how affect and emotions may be systematically reclaimable for gender based development work and feminist politics.

Some of the most important recent critical developments on affect come from neuroscience and scientifically prove that imitation, a keystone to human behavior and learning, can be explained as a result of the brain malleability and the location of proximity of reasoning and emotional responses in the human brain. For instance, based on the principle of the plasticity of the brain, neuroscience has demonstrated that the so-called "mirror neurons" play an important role in prompting imitative behavior, including empathic reactions. Some experiments in clinical psychology have focused on the therapeutic value of emotions to induce desired change in reasoning processes (Greenberg 2008: 51). In the humanities, even rationalist intellectual traditions currently postulate blurred boundaries between reason and emotion; but affect theorists have gone much further to persuasively postulate the independence of circulating affect; a force, they argue, that shapes the social beyond our control (Massumi 1995, 2010; Anderson 2010; Brennan 2004; Ahmed 2010, 2012).[39] This is all to say that different disciplines are currently exploring and demonstrating the fact that affect is a historically situated dynamic phenomenon that contains important information about the social and the individual. Among other things, affective responses of a person or a group are not stable or monolithic; they

---

[38] For a good overview on the "affective turn" you may consult the book by Margaret Wetherell: *Affect and Emotion. A New Social Science Understanding*. Sage Publications: London, 2012.

[39] Massumi and Anderson make a useful distinction between the concepts of 'feelings', 'emotions', and 'affect': 'feelings' are personal, subject to the person's interpretation; 'emotions' are social, a projection or display of a feeling into the world, that is, what makes feelings feel; 'affect' is pre-personal, a non-conscious experience of intensity, a moment of unformed and unstructured potential.

shift permanently subjected to power relations and complex patterns. In fact, as Richard Davidson claims, even our DNA dispositions are by no means determinant of our behavior and unchangeable: positive emotions can be fostered; negative ones located in one part of the brain can be accessed and replaced by emotions from another part of the brain, and our "emotional styles" reshaped (Davidson 2000, 2012). Thus, we need a concept like *feminist emotion* precisely to be able to capture and interpret the shifting and complex nature of affect in the social domain as derived from the experiences of gender as non-male in patriarchal orders; that is, for instance, to grasp the rebellious constituency of women's affective relationship towards gender related power relations and disparities, in situated dynamics.

At this point, it is necessary to briefly further explain some of the premises of my theoretical and interpretative framework through which I approach the happenings and events recounted by Araceli Alonso in Part I. If, as I suggested earlier, incredible personal and collective transformations were triggered in Lunga Lunga, initially without a blueprint specifically designed around *feminist emotion* nor the notion of affect at large that I am referring to, we might then ask: Why would it be important to use the conceptual lenses of *feminist emotion* to explain the happenings in Lunga Lunga and nearby villages? But rather, a more accurate question would be: What is missing in our analysis if we do not develop an interpretation that includes utilization of the concept of *feminist emotion* to explain certain things?

A phenomenological approach to affect facilitates perception of the nuances and specificities of experience, and the meaning entrenched in emotionality that my concept of *feminist emotion* enables us to address. Life, the empirical social level of human existence in socialization, is home to *feminist emotion*. Because affect is intangible, elusive, inevitable, in motion, its manifestations fragmented, and because it cannot be contained nor completely controlled, it can be said to be agency in its primary form. A wide range of variations of emotionality are dispersed throughout fluctuating relational affective processes and exchanges. Emotional processes are utterances of meaning that can be interpreted as containing meaning about the personal and the social, the individual and the communities, about the ways in which people and groups of people are driven by affective practices and culturally and historically rooted repertoires (Denzin 2009: 137). Thus, one can find important meaning in emotionality for the purpose of building politics. For instance, meaning about "freedom", the ways in which people escape social powers through affect and the ways in which they assert the non-fixity of meaning. The epistemological value of emotions as power is the first interpretative move that needs to be taken to re-center women's capacity as agents of their destinies and will in real life. But it is important to elude traditional ontological debates about "women's emotional nature," by focusing on experience and affect as shifting instant nuanced processes of many interacting components.

A fundamental interpretation of affect as it was manifested so productively in Lunga Lunga is that it is pure agency. As such, it just needed "a push" to transform itself from affect into more tangible and specifically channeled forms of agency and action. Put differently, there is a type of emotional agency that women, as human beings whose human existence is utterly conditioned by struggles through gender power relations, cannot avoid. And yet, they cannot "exploit it" consciously to the fullest of its potential unless they unite, for gender-based discrimination is, ultimately, a shared source of their sufferings and struggles.

It was when I met the real women from Lunga Lunga and the other villages that theory made sense to me. A fortunate coincidence put my theoretical academic dedication to studying the emotional aspects of feminism in touch with Araceli Alonso's anthropological and medical expertise and grass-roots dedication in South-East Kenya. As a result, as I explain in the next sections, it became evident to me that the bottom line of what occurs in

Lunga Lunga is that there is a feminist twist to N-HbM's fruitful utilization or management of affect, specifically, positive affect. It made much sense to me to assume that:

> *Feminist emotion*, unknowingly, was set in motion—it was already part of the local women's lives—fostered and channeled in highly productive ways that enhanced the wellbeing of the local women.

The real meaning of such intellectually driven initial conclusions had yet to be revealed to me by the very same Nikumbuke women that I was going to meet during my trip to Lunga Lunga in 2016.

## *Meaning*

It is only now that I have been to Lunga Lunga that I understand why "Nikumbuke" means "Remember me" in Swahili. Affect is ahistorical and ubiquitous, although it is located at contextually and historically situated instances and experiences. By this I mean that the constraints of traditional time and space parameters are irrelevant when trying to understand how affect flows, circulates and shapes the whereabouts of personal, communitarian, and social life. My interpretation is a reading that by no means intends to be the "truth" nor is it merely subjective. In fact, it is the result of a compound of an initial intuition and an intellectual disquisition revisited after my trip to the region, and informed by many years of scientific feminist research and a five-year reflective process on the materials, testimonies, conversations with Araceli Alonso and other people. The conceptual framework that I have outlined in the previous section is meant to delineate some of the general interpretative concepts that, I believe, apply to the N-HbM programs so that it can be perceived as a model—an approach, a strategy and an operative mechanism. But the challenge is much greater than trying to clearly articulate coherent arguments about what has been going on in Lunga Lunga, or even to systematize specific events and achievements. It begins by posing a critical stand that entails deeply questioning the authority of an observer over the realities to be scrutinized. Ironically, it is by departing from such disempowering stand—an objectively speaking—that my own interpretation of the affective nature of what has been occurring in Lunga Lunga makes more sense.

Meaning is physical. Understanding is not authentic, it is incomplete, unreal, false and artificial without the skin. The sound, the tears and laughter, the images of the trees and bushes, the horrors and beauties that are imagined through narrative means before a physical encounter are different when the encounter takes place. A long journey, the idealizations of the mind, the music, the fear, the shake of hands, the distrustful sighs, the dances, the mosquitos, the sweat, the hugs and dust, the clothes and colors, the gifts, the warm sodas, the unsatisfied thirst provide content to intellectually produced meaning through physicality. I could write erudite pages analyzing a well-informed perception of reality and of every word accounted by Araceli Alonso account. But emotionally lived reality and physically felt life is always otherwise; always more accurate, more complex and surprising. Meaning is always other, itself. Meaning is confusing, and is about confusion, for we cannot discern what it is about if we are not open to accept that it is erratic and to some extent, autonomous; that we can only appreciate its references, however partially, by remaining open to affect, emotions and feeling. I have found in affect theory hints and premises to mold my thoughts in a direction that I find rather convincing. However, my own intellectual insights only make sense in the distance of analytical scientific language. Closeness distorts or erases it all. However paradoxically, it is only closeness that, by making intellectual thoughts futile, fuels meaning with a specific relevance, and analytical interpretation with meaning.

The Nikumbuke women took away from me any trace of vertigo of abstraction or futility embedded in my interpretative effort.. My interpretation of N-HbM programs was hollow prior to the physical experience of my encounter with some women in Lunga Lunga and surrounding areas. Before I went to Lunga Lunga, there was no life in my writing. Before I felt the warmth of the women, sweating under the sun and dust, before I cried and laughed over the bravery, endurance and hope of the Nikumbuke women, my discussions about affect and emotions lacked the very same fundamentals that I was pursuing intellectually. I was lifeless. The critic was dead. Discourse was dry. A circle of meaning had to be completed to resurrect me: Meaning became meaningful through affective interpretation and affect acquired meaning as a concept through which intellectual interpretation of the physical dimensions of life and N-HbM made sense.

The notion of ambivalent affective meaning as a form of "bodily reasoning" as well as of cognitive reasoning touched by affect is key to the interpretative and methodological framework that I am proposing to describe the HbAM model. When focusing on affect as the subject matter of scientific research, we are faced with a very elusive component, but also with a tool of incommensurable potential to interpret the world, act upon it, and/or foster action to trigger positive change. In relation to feminist agendas, we must be aware that daily and quotidian responses to gender inequalities may be rather invisible to outsiders or even to the very same people who experience them, for responses are likely to be unwittingly disguised as specific practical claims or manifest just as reactive behavior. Nevertheless, all responsive reactions have deep roots in emotionality, at the individual or collective levels, and are often related to the effects of gender discrimination, even if these effects are not perceptible at a reasoning level. This type of elusiveness of meaning has been persistently pointed at by feminists as gender naturalization processes. Such elusiveness entrenched in many gender-based emotional responses should not

discourage us feminists. On the contrary, I claim that unpercep-
tiveness is often a sign that, alongside acculturation, there is much
*affective matter,* an untamed force (in emotionality) to be
prompted, fostered, accounted for, channeled to effectively
address gender issues, including naturalization. In fact, when
examining details of the outcomes of the events and programs
described by Araceli Alonso through the analytical lenses that I
propose, it is possible to conclude that affective attunements to
what I call *feminist emotion* were unleashed through collective
affective encounters of a diverse sort, and that they facilitated a
forceful emergence of other rather conscious forms of feminism.

Speeded up by an initial absence of rationally perceived and
linguistically mediated awareness of gender issues and disparities,
emotionally originated feminism becomes a solid ground for social
change. I believe that taking affective and emotional processes into
consideration for feminist development agendas is like avoiding a
twist-and-turn secondary road and taking a direct highway.
Making use of *affective matter* and the sediments in affect as
produced by situated gendered emotionality, is precisely what the
N-HbM actions and programs so effectively do. N-HbM's actions
and programs related to gender issues, health and wellbeing in the
Kenyan district of Kwale are somehow "structured" upon affect. As
Alonso's description of the programs and actions proves it, affect
guided the planning and dynamics through; in doing so according
to my interpretation, *feminist emotion* was and still is unavoidably
unleashed, whether regardless of whether the program coordinators and facilitators, or the Nikumbuke women refer to the
existence of *feminist emotion* as such or not. For the purpose of an
analytical interpretation of these facts, the key question is what
kind of feminist theoretical perspective allows us to assert—even if
just partially or inaccurately—that a person's nuanced affect,
deposited and accumulated in emotionality as a sediment, and
circulating beyond the limits of individual bodies is in fact
*rebellious affect* inextricably linked to situated gender.

Whenever addressing gender issues and gender inequalities as a main goal, and whenever women are at the center of action strategies, one must be certain and aware that *feminist emotion* is "there" in affect; that is, as affect tainted by a certain type of rebelliousness directly related to experiences of gender discrimination. As a matter of fact, affect tainted by *feminist emotion* circulates and constantly shapes and reshapes reactions or behavior and fosters communication exchanges and interpersonal connections; it creates meaning. By this I do not mean that one should inevitably refer to *feminist emotion* as something that goes on in one's or others' emotionality or as part of a collective encounter. What I mean is that attunements to gender-induced rebellious affect—*feminist emotion*—might be taking place and that to take this possibility into consideration enhances the chances to productively nurture the rebellious power of certain affective attunements for the purpose of feminist agendas. Ultimately, it is all about being able to foster the emotional sources of feminism as such, not only as a reasoning process. Put it differently, the value of *feminist emotion* as a conceptual tool for the purpose of political action is that exposure to gender discrimination and oppression produce what scientists call "affective sedimentations" in the human brain, and that affective attunements to such gender sedimentations or a non-reasoning "knowledge" of gender issues may occur precisely when they are induced by situations or dynamics that foster positive affect (Davidson and McEwen 2012). Here is another interpretative key to N-HbM programs:

> Affective attunements to gender sedimentations is at the core of social mobilization for development and for shaping the specific meaning of wellbeing beyond pre-assumptions.

In the next sections, I will illustrate how the N-HbM actions and programs so powerfully narrated by Araceli Alonso in Part I, made use of the transformative and cascade effect of *feminist emotion*. In illustrating this fact, it will become evident that things often occur independently of our thoughts about them, because Alonso and other facilitators did not have in mind *feminist emotion* nor affect as such when they fostered the deep transformations that are taking place in Lunga Lunga and surroundings. To me this is an important lesson to learn by any proud critic or outside observer who may think that they can just systematically implement a development model previously carefully conceived, even if it integrates a methodology to make the best use of affect. But, it is also a confirmation that there is a certain type of affective accuracy about gender that needs to be scrutinized through a theoretical lens that is able to refer to intangibility with certain conceptual precision. This is a very important matter because affect, such slippery, ambivalent and rather unpredictable material dimension of experience, is an untamed transformative force of daily constituencies that makes life livable for many people in the midst of/in spite of gender discrimination and oppression.

The only way that I can think of to approach an analysis of the simultaneous vastness and simplicity of life is to take into consideration affect and the derived concept that I am proposing—*feminist emotion*—as a category to capture the infiniteness of gendered affective nuances. Theory is necessary to understand how and when *feminist emotion* is manifest, and to pragmatically deepen into or reinforce the areas of life that it may enlighten. *Feminist emotion* could also be a useful concept to shed clarity onto certain dimensions of grassroots work where women are engaged; dimensions that may otherwise pass unnoticed although they entail a real potential to build sustainable changes. No doubt. But sometimes theory coupled with physical encounters with people and reality forces us to humbly accept the shortcomings of intellectual processes and to surrender to other ways in which knowledge, in its purest and crudest lived form, is abruptly uncovered and revealed to us.

## A Model

When trying to define a model of grass-roots work that un-wittingly and effectively channels gendered rebellious affect and ambivalent shifting meaning for the sake of promoting women's empowerment, the following questions arise: Does utilization of *feminist emotion* as an interpretative tool entail putting a restraining rational cord to a force that is utterly free by its very affective nature? Will a rationally reasoned identification of *feminist emotion* on the part of Nikumbuke women bring about unexpected complications and on-the-ground counterproductive effects for feminist agendas? What could facilitators of N-HbM programs do, provided that *feminist emotion* is *a priori* analytical interpretative action oriented tool? How does our perception of the ongoing events in Lunga Lunga and nearby villages change if we examine them through the lenses of *feminist emotion* as explained above?

Before I visited Lunga Lunga it was clear to me that affect should just flourish freely so that it may produce certain forms of knowledge as well as a bodily relationship to knowledge through interactions in which all the senses are involved, and subjective encounters that eventually give way to what Araceli Alonso so poignantly refers to as "transversal leaderships" related to gender issues. As I attempt to address the above mentioned dilemmas to get closer to delineating the *Health by All Means* (HbAM) model, it is highly likely that I will be confronted with some philosophical and methodological contradictions. For instance: On the one hand, facilitators of the HbAM model must learn to see and interpret *feminist emotion* so that attunements to it in their field work may be fostered productively; on the other hand, to allow individual and collective change to take place, they may have to let *feminist emotion* manifest itself untamed, circulating freely at a non-reasoned level, simultaneously visible and invisible through affect. So, considering that it is not crystal clear what to do and how to proceed, one must wonder if the hypothetical HbAM model can really be replicated.

Let me begin by stating that two interpretative levels must be differentiated to understand what may happen with and through the circulating affect that often emerges naturally and spontaneously: 1. One level concerns facilitators who set the initial ground for the development of the programs and later supervise them as mediators—not as "teachers;" 2. The other level relates to the beneficiaries, the local women who become the main actors, real agents, or facilitators and teachers for each other. We must keep this two-level distinction in mind for methodological purposes, although it is artificially created. As I will explain and illustrate later, the two levels are highly diffused and merge into each other in the HbAM model:

> Facilitators are interpreters, mediators, and strategists; beneficiaries are real strategists for wellbeing: interpreters, mediators of their own and others' life changes and behavior.

For facilitators to apprehend or detect *feminist emotion* so that its transformative affective power to address feminist agendas and gender equality goals is not diluted, non-dualistic thinking is necessary; that is, a breakthrough of the sharp conceptual separations traditionally placed between reason and emotions, and the like. Among other things, interpretative efforts should be directed towards discerning instances, utterances, behavior, discourse that may seem tainted by an affective resistance to social gender hierarchies and oppressive hegemonies. Nevertheless, a sort of *affective reasoning* regarding the observed events and perceived affect must also take place on the part of facilitators as the means to approach the ambivalence of meaning. It is about allowing an attunement to one's affective responses and perceptions of circulating affect while interpreting the attunements of others.

The N-HbM programs' director and other facilitators did not name *feminist emotion* as such nor spoke about affect as a gendered force. It does not matter because, as I explain in some detail in the next sections, *feminist emotion* did in fact emerged and had an incidence in the community and personal transformations in Lunga Lunga. It doesn't really matter whether *feminist emotion* is taken as the means or as an end. What is most important to understand is that there is a dimension of reality that often passes unnoticed, partly because women or poor women in this case are the protagonists. It is essential to comprehend that the nature of certain events that occurred *in* the real world within certain specific blurred time/space spheres speak about the surpassing of any kind of imagined, imposed or material contours. This is precisely why we need a concept that is molded to such required understanding to allow for a more precise interpretation of the elusiveness of daily nuances and encounters. The encounters will take place anyhow, but procedural affective feminist happenings and changes may pass unnoticed as such if we do not adopt a concept—*feminist emotion*—that provides closeness to them by conceiving them as an inescapable possibility.

A model requires replication. My training in the humanities has convinced me of the importance of giving a name to realities so that they "exist" in individual or collective imagination. Discourse, language, naming becomes essential. It is our duty as critics to provide the means through which others may incite similar transformations elsewhere. The expression and the concept captured by the two words: *feminist* and *emotion* is thus, unavoidable; there is a sort of authoritarian power of language over us but it is a friendly one; language is a good ally. Among other things, in the context of N-HbM programs, to name *feminist emotion* as something that is within the lives of the women of Lunga Lunga region sheds light onto the intricacies of how inevitably gender advocacy and women's leaderships sprouted. One reason for this is that the concept of *feminist emotion* brings to the forefront of analysis a nuanced notion of affect that may be very productive for gender equality and justice-building purposes. In Lunga Lunga, *feminist emotion* was intuitively nurtured by facilitators through a series of health intervention and training programs, a fact that greatly enhanced women's empowerment and wellbeing, and made a big difference for over one thousand women and their relatives. The process through which these happenings occurred could be described in abstract terms as follows: Facilitators of the N-HbM programs first managed to set positive affect in motion through the programs; and second, channeled its incredible potential as related to gender, into diverse additional activities that enhanced both the programs themselves and women's empowerment. Affect derived into a reinforcement of gender awareness, community leaderships, and advocacy actions related to gender equality. Such an outcome would be sufficient to illustrate my theoretical proposal on the importance of affect touched by a specific kind of rebellious affective component—*feminist emotion*—as a constituent of the HbAM model; but there are additional important observations to make.

It is important to emphasize that not having a blueprint for promoting gender awareness, as it has been the case of the N-HbM programs, may in fact be an advantageous departure if the key facilitators are properly trained on gender issues and global health as related to development. Strikingly, the N-HbM facilitators enabled *feminist emotion* just by paying attention to affect and emotions throughout the human exchanges that took place in different occasions; particularly, they nurtured the positive affect that emanated from collective encounters and in doing so, they prompted incipient non-reasoning feminist consciousness without the need to conduct extensive training on gender issues. Araceli Alonso focused on the promotion of women's health as a primary task and stepping stone to wellbeing instead of implementing a pre-set agenda to promote gender awareness towards, for instance, diverse forms of gender-based violence. This move happened to be a very smart way to elude likely to happen culturally-based resistance to feminist agendas coming from outsiders. As Alonso so graphically describes it, a specific aspect of women's health, maternal health became the initial "thread" to many other ways to unravel such complicated matters as life-risking birth giving, mother/child disease, poor nutrition or domestic violence. To this date, this unraveling of other deeply culturally embedded and complex matters like genital mutilation or forced child marriage continues with outstanding outcomes.

Nine years into the ongoing community changes of Lunga Lunga and surroundings makes it possible to authoritatively catalogue the occurrences as an unstoppable untangling of the skein of gender awareness. At the risk of sounding circular in my arguments, I believe that the forceful emergence of *feminist emotion* is at the very core of the gradual emergence of diverse degrees and types of gender awareness in Lunga Lunga.

## Philosophy

**Knowledge** and **Joy** are the two igniting forces behind the deep personal, communal and social transformations that have taken place since 2010 in the seven villages of the District of Kwale, Kenya, where N-HbM operates: Lunga Lunga, Godo, Perani, Mpakani, Jirani, Umoja, and Maasailand.

### *Knowledge*

The 'health camps' are the first activities that ignited the creation of the micro NGO, N-HbM, and the development of its programs. In 2010, the health camps were the seed to give birth to the HbAM model. Araceli Alonso's decision to begin grassroots actions with massive informal gatherings—the 'health camps'—derived from her own belief in the power of direct human encounters and friendships. She had participated in a *Rafiki* program, a virtual friendship exchange through which she virtually met a woman from Perani named Mariamu. One day she decided to travel to meet Mariamu in person and initiated a long journey to the distant region of Lunga Lunga, unknown to her by then. It was while she was there physically as a visitor for the first time and listened to Mariamu's worries and problems, as well as to those of other local women, that she came up with the idea of the camps. And the camps were going to give way to N-HbM unfolding. Thus, the very first step of what was later to become the comprehensive N-HbM programs consisted of organizing three health camps of approximately one hundred women participants from three different villages, each of them aimed at jointly examining specific needs related poverty, harsh living conditions, and health related matters. It all started at these initial massive camps.

Araceli Alonso powerfully explains in Part I that since the very beginning she adopted the *Umoja* approach. *Umoja* implies fostering the intrinsic human potential for solidarity and unity, and most important, promoting people's capacity for enacting positive communication through self-reflection and empathic behavior. Attendees to the camps knew little about each other; facilitators did not know what was the appropriate guiding structure of the gatherings, but they tactfully avoided using any sort of hierarchy. They refused to be treated like guests. For instance, contrary to local civility codes and unspoken racial dynamics, when lunch was to be distributed, facilitators requested that everybody eat and drink the same food and beverages: warm sodas and water, rice and beans for all. The local participants, beneficiaries, and attendees of the three camps initially were a bit puzzled by this move. Ultimately, the facilitators' refusal to be treated as guests ended up becoming a cornerstone for friendship to be cultivated among them and thus, an important step towards the positive chain of actions and events to follow. Affection and trust for one another flourished later, somehow fueled with such initial moves. The move to share the available food in the very same terms for all equally was a necessary grain in a mountain of sand. The decision was made through pure and simple common sense and empathic feeling. However, its impact was much greater than expected:

> Affection, trust and friendship, fostered non-hierarchically during the first camps of 2010, became the very foundation of the programs for the years to come.

Since the very beginning, the *Umoja* approach necessarily implied that facilitators had to confront the great challenge of sorting out and working around knowledge hierarchies and authority issues. They became just learning facilitators, mediators, channeling friends, or as Araceli Alonso puts it, "conductors of a symphony" that was being composed and was going to be performed by the local women. Beneficiaries became "authors of their own symphony", "owners of their orchestra."

Besides the above mentioned instance of the meals, there were other means through which a highly positive and productive atmosphere was created at the camps. For instance, cautious handling of money related dynamics was essential. Alonso prohibited students and the other facilitators to give money to any of the local people under any circumstances. Friendship was to be maintained above all; any kind of monetary gesture, no matter how well intentioned or small, would have destroyed the possibility of an equal-to-equal friendship. The role of Bendettah Thomas, the local leader who was to become the overall N-HbM coordinator, was also extremely important to "train" Lunga Lunga women about this rule and inform them that there was a system of small available fellowships they all could apply for, and that they should not ask for money directly.

Araceli Alonso's narration of the above mentioned occurrences vividly confirms that a spontaneous unfolding of awareness of the structural connections between poverty and health, and about wellbeing, started at the camps. People project symbolism, meaning about the world unbalances into things, gestures, context. Context is determinant to meaning, and meaning is multifaceted, ambivalent. There is much to reflect upon why certain apparently minimal happenings, gestures or objects have relevance within the larger scope of N-HbM comprehensive approach and strategies.

Social Exchange Theory helps to further understand what the camps made possible: First, why the joint activities of the first camps derived into reaffirmed and strengthened solidarity; second, why the positive feelings fostered through various simple gestures eliminated *a priori* socio-cultural barriers, and contributed to create a highly productive context for knowledge exchange It is possible to state that within the exchange context of N-HbM first camps, the relational conditions described above may have fueled certain type of positive affect and positive emotionality at large, and facilitated its circulation among the group of participants. Such personal and collective positive affective experiences enhanced a constructive emotional display, and provoked a spontaneous revision of some social codes and community norms. Social codes and community norms are not just subject to local civility rule and customary law but also molded by unspoken global structural differences of a world shaped by deep power unbalance. A structural-relational approach to social exchange places an emphasis on positional differences in felt emotion as directly linked to exchanges and networks at the local level in the context of global dynamics. As a result, a focus is placed upon power and status. For example, increased power and status result in positive emotions, and decreased power and status lead to negative emotions (Lawler and Thye 1999: 225). This approach may apply to the contextual relational dynamics of N-HbM first camps as follows: Positive affect and positive emotionality at large emanated from a power-status reversal that was unplanned but intentionally recreated at the micro-level of the camps. As a result, those who had less power and status within postcolonial global world dynamics—the local women of Lunga Lunga—were uplifted as equals to those who symbolized power—facilitators—regardless of whether power was encapsulated as academic knowledge, money, racial whiteness, northern geopolitical precedence, etc. This is not a reversal of hierarchies but rather, an equalizing dynamic. But this explanation is only partially satisfactory, because by exclusively paying attention to structural relational dynamics between people, one misses an important piece of information about how emotional encounters and relational exchanges are shaped and developed into specific outcomes.

I have serious doubts that a sharp analytical division between emotional processes and contextual relationality fully explains the dynamics of the first camps and the happenings that followed. It is also necessary to assume that a sort of neutral or power-free terrain sprouted out of the incorporation of certain gestures, and that it may have facilitated a very productive temporary suspension of all sort of hierarchies. Although the structural unbalance of the contemporary global world and their direct consequences in people's lives are indisputable, there is much to discuss about their effect and about how each community and individual experiences them. For instance, it is limiting to conclude that the positive feelings expressed by the participants of the camps were mostly due to unspoken power unbalance and status reversals. For one thing, we cannot assume that power and status are equally important for everybody, at a conscious or unconscious level; there are many diverse ways in which power is internalized, shared, managed, viewed, imagined, filtered, experienced, expressed.

Power is diversely tainted or molded by gender and other interacting identity-situated and historical factors as well as by many intercepting elements that also shape affect and emotional processes. For instance, very specific objects and gestures can have a strong irradiating effect onto people and groups. As philosopher Alphonso Lingis has so beautifully explained, just like people project sentiments onto things, things irradiate meaning, energy onto people and other beings on their own, without people's intervention. This is a cascade effect that is often unseen and unacknowledged. Our culturally shaped Cartesian ways of thinking about the material world impedes the perception of irradiating connections that we, humans, have with the material world and that the non-human and material world has with us. Fortunately, there are other ontological ways of examining physicality so that, as Lingis puts it, "The reality of things is not confined within their contours" (Lingis 2010: 13). In my view, Lingis' observation indistinctively applies to the invisible socio-cultural contours of material objects and their strictly material finitude. Everything, and any dimension of our existence is inter-connected. But how does such material inter-connectedness apply to what occurred at the camps?

The material "participants" of the camps—a bottle of soda, a plate of rice and beans, a dollar bill—may have created an effect that expanded beyond the interactive moment of two or more people. During the real event of the camps in Lunga Lunga, such an effect partly derived from the socio-cultural meaning inscribed in the object, the exchange moment and surrounding circumstances, individuals' relationship to them, the momentary pleasure that the objects triggered, and the local and global contexts where the objects were located. But the influence that objects have on humans is also related to an inherent human capacity to identify with and through material culture in/through affect (Harris and

Sorensen 2010: 148). In fact, the positive emotional impact of a simple gesture to take, give or refuse a bottle of soda, a plate of food, or a dollar bill could be said to encapsulate meaning that cannot be completely explained by neither Cartesian nor structural relational approaches. During the camps, the irradiating power of objects and gestures was like an "emanation" of the object and gestures themselves. The presence or absence of the object and the enactment of gestures was precisely what set positive affect in motion in ways that could not be utterly predicted. However, the intrinsic positive power of ambivalent affective meaning as a cohesive element of the group was intuitively anticipated by Araceli Alonso.

When discussing affect in terms of its autonomous power, as affect theorists would urge us to do, it is fundamental to also extend such reasoning to objects themselves, and to the relation-ships between objects and subjects; people and the atmosphere created at a specific coexistence of people, places and things (Harris and Sorensen 2010: 152). Thus, an affective encounter cannot be fully explained without referring to the hierarchical relationships that people have with objects, not just with each other, as well as about the unperceived tyrannical power of the objects towards people. The camp dynamics were about social power, status alterations and equalizing dynamics, but they also entailed a sort of liberation of the individuals and the group from the material authority of objects. A surrendering to the pleasures of such liberation is precisely what allowed positive affect to freely flow.

Power and status among the individuals in the group and their relationship to the objects were very much interlinked at the camps as follows: The obliteration of objects fed new power-status dynamics where power-status or the objects were no longer important and were replaced by the forceful energy of the effect of positive affective human interactions as well as of people's interactions with the objects and the materiality of the camps during the events. The act of eating the same food and drinking water or soda indistinctly by all members of the group, regardless of status, occupied a secondary position. Bottles and plates were relegated to trivial functionary objects for all to share the a-hierarchical moment that they were all immersed in. The group was free at last, momentarily, from the tyrannical hegemonic powers of globalized worldly dynamics that impede social harmony by creating socio-economic unbalance, fueling injustice and oppression, and nurturing the irradiating blocking influence of objects, goods and money. In sum, when interpreting the happenings described by Alonso we must keep in mind that:

> Positive affect was fully allowed to flourish and was carefully nurtured; as a result, its influential effect expanded through the interactional collective context that included a complex trans-relational exchange among people and other elements and material objects.

Positive affect is a primary social equalizer and temporary status eliminator of the HbAM model. As such, affect certainly contains information about what feminist theorist Clare Hemmings refers to as the "qualitative experience of the social world," but also—I would add—it refers to experiences related to the materiality and physicality of the world (Hemmings 2005: 549). Affect is an embodied experience that transforms and exceeds social subjection. One can visualize its effect as spanning in circles: People feel better because positive affect circulates by transcending material and structural relational hierarchies, and affect circulates more intensely, making people feel better, and because people feel better in relation to themselves, the others and the objects that surround them.

The camps can be catalogued as "affective fields," as described by Harris and Sorersen:

The relationship between agents, where something or somebody is stimulating an emotional response in a causal set of events. As such, affective fields are dynamic and generative, or provoked, changing the state of affairs in a given situation. Affective fields are produced between people, places and things, and they may thus vary depending on the relations in which they are enmeshed (Harris and Sorensen 2010: 150).

The circulation of positive affect in the "affective fields" of the camps, facilitated the emergence of a sense of ownership towards knowledge on the part of the local women. Araceli Alonso tells us that right after the first camps, the women of Lunga Lunga requested a basic health training program not because they "thought" they needed it, but because they "knew" they needed it. In other words, the women who participated in the camps had ownership towards knowledge, not to supplant the facilitators' role as teachers but because they expressed their authority towards their own lives by expressing a desire to acquire a specialized kind of knowledge. Facilitators and beneficiaries, although tied to differentiated roles, were horizontally equalized as agents when it came down to deciding what kind of knowledge was needed, for whom and why, and when the training was to be imparted. Put it differently, beneficiaries and facilitators were united in *affective agency* leading towards knowledge sharing. It was all facilitated by the non-hierarchical encounters in which minimal gestures and material objects played a major role. As I have suggested, something other than a simple reversal of knowledge hierarchies took place during N-HbM first health camps. In fact, it was not a reversal at all:

A highly productive strategic suspension or avoidance of knowledge hierarchies set affect in motion, and such force was nurtured by facilitating the collective and productive circulation of affect.

Issues of knowledge authority, the limitations of knowledge, and the functionality of knowledge were not real obstacles at the camps nor subjects for discussion. Knowledge hierarchies were simply overturned, disrupted, and eluded. Local women's experiences were listened to as *authoritative knowledge*; they were the one and only factor that had incidence in the decision-making process over what type of training was to be imparted. Furthermore, it was just them who decided that they, in fact, needed training in the first place. The collective affective experience of the camps through which Lunga Lunga women came to claim the acquisition of knowledge itself as a pressing need, was validated as authoritative knowing. First, because it was the only script used by facilitators to decide next steps; second, because such first steps were going to guide the by then still incipient programs of which they were going to have complete ownership in the years to come. Thus, another key to our incipient delineation of the HbAM model is:

> The *Umoja* approach adopted in N-HbM programs, the collective experience of sharing needs and actively listening to each other regardless of cultural, linguistic, ethnic, nationality-related, age, and religious differences is ultimately about the very validation of the local women's *experiential knowledge* as *authoritative knowledge*, and of them as agents of knowledge.

One can figuratively say that the local women began writing the unspoken script of what we call the HbAM model. All they needed was a place to express their authority towards their own lives and towards knowledge itself as a necessary prioritized commodity to combat and reverse the hardships of poverty. The relevance of Nikumbuke women's claim to knowledge acquisition as a priority in their lives during and after the camps becomes utterly meaningful when analyzed in the context of their living circumstances, plagued with scarcity of commodities and very difficult living conditions. Their claim and their experiential knowledge are in fact the real protagonists of the processes promoted through N-HbM programs. The scientific knowledge about health, nutrition and physiology that facilitators were soon to share with them in the "health promoters training programs' can just be said to be *complementary knowledge*, one more element or utility to promote wellbeing; just like a solar energy lamp or a water tank, carefully placed on the road to wellbeing of the inhabitants of the Lunga Lunga geographic area.

Within the type of knowledge dynamics that sprouted at the camps through the *Umoja* approach, all agents—all the participants—developed the ability to recognize diverse types of knowledge in non-hierarchical ways; most important, they all learned to see themselves and others as valuable and equal agents of knowledge as they appreciated the complementary nature of diverse types of knowledge. For instance, facilitators learned that scientific knowledge was just complementary to experiential knowledge and that affective knowing was an integral part to scientific knowledge; a core to its subject matter. In sum, as standpoint theory would have it: The successful outcome of the original health camps that gave rise to other educational actions in follow-up *cascade-intervention* has much to do with a communicative collective experience in which the "inhabitants of the margins" are the privileged knowers about themselves and the(ir) world but, in relation to the camps, also about the content of the programs yet to be developed (Harding 1986). This is one reason why:

> The university/scientific back up of facilitators is essential to the HbAM model, for it was the venue to develop a curricu-

lum for the training that women request and to perform the training itself.

Communication was facilitated because positive affect was set in motion and was channeled to productively circulate in a specific affective field or context fostered by the dynamics described above. But *feminist emotion* was also a crucial component of the dynamics provoked by positive circulating affect. One thing is indisputable to me: the central realization of the local women who participated in the camps was that they were disempowered because they lacked information about primary issues related to their own bodies, health concerns and struggles as women, and that their very first need was to address and reverse these facts. Maternal health was one of the recurrent themes at the camp gatherings, like Araceli Alonso recalls; a major concern that later turned out to be the pathway, the "thread" as Alonso names it, for women to recover a sense of ownership towards their own wellbeing towards the kind of wellbeing to be sought and achieved collectively as "Nikumbuke Women."

Shared affective experiences at the camps fostered receptivity to new information about specific matters, such as cutting the umbilical cord. Affective communication became a breakthrough of gender-related barriers that blocked Nikumbuke Women's self-esteem and empowerment thanks to the fact that a component of affect that I call *feminist emotion* was, inevitably, present as part of the emotional processes. I would say that the means of storytelling and spontaneous recalling of experiences around maternal issues that took place during the camps was the means through which women recovered a sense of ownership over their lives as well as a sense of authorship about their lives as women (Mackenzie 2000). On the one hand, positive affect triggered a sense of belonging that was crucial for the soon to-be-created transitional communities of other N-HbM programs, as well as the hope for self-desired changes. On the other hand, such process of self and collective examination spontaneously revealed awareness, resistance to gender-caused disempowerment, and led to an ability to reverse it, agency expressed through/as a claim to knowledge: they requested a training program. Here is where *feminist emotion* interceded as an affective component that facilitated gender awareness to germinate from the affective process of the camps at large. Simply put: To become more empowered all that the local women needed was someone to respectfully listen to them as equals and acknowledge them as agents of knowledge. The act of listening on the part of facilitators took place in the context of collective affective fields in which diverse types of knowledge—including scientific knowledge—interacted conjunctively and non-hierarchically.

Let us recapitulate. Knowledge is "situated," not universalizable, both individually and collectively. The ground for alternative signification about some social issues related to the worries of the local women in the area of Lunga Lunga—health issues at first—was set up through the irradiating effects of positive affect as well as rebellious affect—triggered by gender and its confluences with multiple factors of socialization and inter-relationality—which can be said to be colored, induced, molded by the specific component that I call *feminist emotion* Ownership and authorship of the N-HbM actions was set up through the initial affective experience of the camps where individual and collective experiential knowledge was validated as authoritative. Furthermore, the authority of experiential knowledge was expressed and seen by the participants as inextricably linked to their gendered experiences, a fact that can be interpreted both as a sign and a trigger of *feminist emotion*. The collective experience of the camps, stirred up the emergence of affect whose ambiguity can be interpreted as coming from a universally gender-rooted sedimentation in emotionality.

Since the group of participants consisted of women from very diverse ethnic groups who did not use to mix at all before the camps, there is an additional epistemic value to be discerned from the emergence of *feminist emotion* as a component of affect during N-HbM first health camps: It prompted inter-community harmony or laid the ground for peace-building; it was a determinant element in/for overcoming community, cultural and ethnic boundaries.. The ultimate outcome is that the means to peace-building—understood as fostering collaboration and solidarity and leading to community wellbeing—fruitfully sprouted amidst traditionally separated communities. First, peace became a specifically situated reality in Lunga Lunga during the camps; later, peace and wellbeing would expand to a much larger radio of influence, reaching six other villages.

From the theoretical framework that I previously outlined, peace is the very possibility of overcoming identity and the limiting contours of the self; that is, identity marks as dissociating conditioners that constrain the self into all-but-potentiality: For instance, class or race; class, defined by Cynthia Cockburn as "ownership and lack of ownership over the means of production and differences in relationship to property and wealth" over which war and conflict often germinate; and race, as "the outcome of a social process of differentiation, hierarchization and disempowerment upon the bases of skin color and phenotype, as well as territorial association, ethnicity, religion, national identification" (Cockburn 2007: 7). Incredibly enough, the forceful potential of affect during the first health camps, specifically, the sharing of an affective agency-related component directly linked to shared women's experiences of gender issues, took roots so deeply amidst participants that collaboration and solidarity, as peace-building dynamics, became the fuel and engine to develop the next actions and programs to come of N-HbM. Why?

"Foreignicity" and its "ethnopower" relations were recurrently temporary suspended as constraining factors, clearing the way for agency and potentiality. As feminists have amply demonstrated, identity intersections, including structures of economic and gendered power, are mutually constitutive and determine group dynamics that are likely to be tainted by conflict. We may say that a contextual elimination of ethno-power relations took place during the first camps and allowed for new identity and new self-perceptions to emerge. Conflict was neutralized through shared affect. As Araceli Alonso explains it, the outcome of such complex identity revisiting process was the fact that the very same participants requested a basic health education program to address all sorts of concerns about wellbeing, not just illness or strictly health problems. In other words, a comprehensive approach to health was somehow conceived and demanded by the very same women who needed it. This is how the *unfolding type of planning* of N-HbM started; other training actions and health related diverse types of assistance began. Some of the next initiatives were: A train-the-trainers program for community health promoters; the Nikumbuke Mama Toto Mobile Clinic; a permanent health post that was to later become the Nikumbuke Women's Health Center, together with a tailoring school, a library, dwellings, a gathering area, a guest house, and a hairdressing school/salon; a theater company; a soccer league; a Moringa tree-plantation; gender-based violence prevention campaigns; disease prevention campaigns; distribution of water tanks and mosquito nets; a new primary education school; an educational fellowship program for adolescent girls; etc.

There is still more to say about the first health camps as the activity that ignited the creation of the micro NGO, N-HbM, and the development of several programs to this date. As I mentioned before, there was neither a pre-set agenda nor a set up plan about what needed to be done in the region—although a thorough initial anthropological research was conducted by Araceli Alonso, after her first trip to Lunga Lunga. As women expressed their view points, shared their experiences, and told their life stories, facilitators listened and took note for the yet-to-be-designed programs. Incipient leaderships were forged at the camps too, to judge by Alonso's powerful recalling and reflections of the current active engagement of over one thousand "Nikumbuke Women," as they call themselves. Besides the fact that, as I discussed above, collectively, women requested the formal health training, some women manifested a strong sense of self-confidence in different ways. For instance, some of them rejected money for their attendance to the camps and instead asked to be rewarded in kind, with rice and beans, arguing that it would be a better way to avoid their husbands' control of the earnings. This is a clear example of what I have referred to elsewhere as *stealthy rebellions* or behavioral manifestations of *feminist emotion*; an example of a gender-motivated non-reasoning subversive act or gesture of a feminist sort (Langle de Paz 2011). It was all prompted or at least reinforced by the informal educational activity of the camps that, as I have demonstrated, turned out to preeminently be about creating a communicative non-hierarchical affective environment of highly productive affective fields (Burkitt 2012: 461).

The central subject matter of the camps was in fact, *experiential knowledge* itself; the outcome, greater and productively channeled gender awareness, the notion of wellbeing itself, reinforced leaderships, and incipient peace-building; the means, *feminist emotion*. Very early on, in the camps sessions, it became clear for the facilitators that women blamed gendered socialization for certain health issues and problems they endured. Just as it was to become clear, three years later into the N-HbM programs, that the group of health promoters who participated in a domestic violence workshop knew how unequivocally domestic violence and other forms of gender-based violence were different sides of the same phenomenon related to gender-based discrimination and structural violence (Langle de Paz 2016: 187-203).

The emergence of spontaneous leaderships of women who wanted to become community leaders after the camps, can be interpreted as a natural and inevitable outcome of a productive handling of affect that included personal and collective attunements to feminist emotion.

Let us now envision the simile of an artist creating an abstract painting. The brush freely flows to produce shades, lines, textures, color compositions, one pictorial world within an otherworld. The artwork emerges spontaneously; emotions directly projected from the soul onto the canvas by the mediation of a skillful hand. But for the final product to become a perfect intuitive equilibrium of lines and colors, textures and shades that communicates "something" powerful, it is likely that the hand has devoted many hours to becoming skillful, to learning or exploring drawing and many other painting techniques. Just as it is certain that life experiences have left imprints on the artist's soul that are turned, by the skillful hand, into an artistic composition. Free flow and technique; intuition, experience and specialized artistic knowledge work together, a powerful alliance to produce the work of art. The free expression of the soul projected on the canvas as a piece of art needs the hand, but the hand needs to be freed from the stiffness of technique for the composition and creative process to take place as a liberating experience. This is how the artistic experience of the artist will find its own perfection for the painting to be art, to communicate something as art.

Perhaps a beautiful locally authored work of art was about to be developed when Araceli Alonso first arrived in Lunga Lunga yet, another way to look at it is to assume that "the work of art" was already in the making prior to Alonso's visit; it just needed to be seen and fueled. In any case, it is for us, authors of this book, to try to explain the key elements and factors that contributed to its marvel: What created the optimal conditions through which the women from the Lunga Lunga area were skillful enough to pursue their "artwork" by projecting their knowledge and soul onto the "canvas"?

Allowing or promoting affect to freely circulate through situated respectful human interactions where hierarchies are temporarily suspended, as was the case with the events in the health camps, can be said to be equivalent to the "skillful strategy" of the artist in the simile. On the one hand, the circulation of affect, as I have explained it, gave way to the birth of other specific activities and actions after the camps: the health promoters training program, the Aya Ukumbi Theater about health-related issues, and even the idea of installing water-tanks. As Araceli Alonso recalls, it was at the very beginning of the programs that some women felt empowered by the camps and began requesting *knowledge*, the acquisition of useful health-related knowledge to improve their wellbeing; it was during a brainstorming of ideas to overcome challenges about water that Mama Margret came up with the idea of the water-tanks over other options like a community-run well; it was also at the initial stage of the programs that they spontaneously began enacting the knowledge they had acquired through diverse theater performances.

The fact that theater is currently a very effective instrumental N-HbM program to address gender issues like domestic violence or force marriage and child trafficking for labor exploitation does not mean that theater must always be integrated into new adapted versions of the HbAM model elsewhere; as Alonso states, diverse ethnic groups prefer different means of expressions—i.e., the Maasai prefer singing. Thus, another important aspect of the HbAM model is:

> To create the context through which women feel good enough to engage in creative productions around acquired knowledge and to engage others, so that knowledge expands creatively.

N-HbM camps provided the grounds for the inevitable affective reality of *feminist emotion* to take over and project itself on "the canvas." A certain kind of affect touched by a rebellious component directly related to gender socializations—*feminist emotion*—emerged when the conditions were optimal and safe, experiential and scientific knowledge leveled, and when the Nikumbuke Women, the "artists," were free and freed by affect to gain clarity towards their feelings and the others' and express it all. The conjunction of all these elements was a productive forceful combination with positive centrifuge effects that would lead to "the work of art": N-HbM yet to come actions and programs that fostered very positive personal changes and inter/intra-community harmony and wellbeing.

If one takes into consideration my proposal that the N-HbM programs made use of *feminist emotion* even if its operational sources and means were unnamed as such, in the context of health promotion agendas with a focus on gender issues, the *Umoja* approach enabled at least the following important outcomes:

1. Gender was transcended through affect in diverse contexts and multiple occasions;
2. Affect was used to promote such processes and their contagious effects extended to all agents, including the international facilitators of the programs (Hemmings 2005: 559);
3. The work carried out with/through affect was utterly necessary for the women of Lunga Lunga to feel ownership towards the very notion of their own wellbeing;
4. Leaderships and empowerment were inextricably linked to an enhanced awareness of the structural nature of gender oppression.

As explained above, many of the affective manifestations that took place since the very first event of the health camps promoted by Araceli Alonso were infused by *feminist emotion*. The concept of *feminist emotion* is useful to capture a real potential for personal and social transformations that otherwise may pass unnoticed as an inextricable dimension of gender non-reasoned awareness in affect. By no means am I arguing that a "second class" non-reasoning feminist type of consciousness should be the only goal for development work with women. I am arguing that when prioritizing the emergence of full rational gender awareness is utterly complicated or even counterproductive due to socio-cultural reasons—as is the case of the rural communities in Lunga Lunga area—being attentive to what occurs at the level of affect and how it relates to non-reasoned gender awareness can be a very effective shortcut to foster and strengthen personal and community change towards wellbeing.

Here is another recommendation derived from the HbAM model:

> Program facilitators need to work towards an understanding of a nuanced notion of affect. This entails the recognition that affect has many components, including *feminist emotion*, a rebellious component that speaks of women's non-acceptance or resistance to situated patriarchal norm and values. It is emotional knowledge about gender.

A nuanced notion of affect requires attention to its qualitative nature or "texture," moving away from traditional and monolithic conceptions of emotion (Sedgwick 2003). And to do so, besides analyzing events through the theoretical lenses that I propose, it is necessary to be perceptive and knowledgeable about the intersections between health, wellbeing, gender, and many other circumstantial and identity factors that interact—for good and for bad—during the processes through which affect emerges:

> Affect is likely to become a catalyst for diverse forms of women's leadership and empowerment when it is set in motion, but it must be carefully channeled through scientifically informed comprehensive approaches to intervention.

I can only offer my own explanation of the utilization of affect that shaped the core mechanisms of N-HbM programs to complement Araceli Alonso's ethnographic narration. My hope is that my interpretation will contribute to a replicable usage of its philosophical approach and structural components; its "organic" unfolding into holistic comprehensive intervention, through which over one thousand women have managed to define change and change their lives as well as the lives of their communities for good.

The type of intervention that gradually developed after the first health camps is referred to by Araceli Alonso as having a "circular structure" and taking place at three levels simultaneously: local grassroots level, national government level, and international academic level; a circularity that contributed to stirring up women's capacity to act upon what they were learning about health issues and related matters. My own interpretation of this appreciation is that the process of empowerment through learning also concerned each woman's attunement to her own *affective knowledge* of the fact that health is gendered and related to gendered structural discrimination, in addition to a collective attunement with each other's similar realizations. Women's capacity for action was enhanced through the process of recognizing themselves, first, as gendered knowledge subjects, and later, as knowledge agents on gender issues related to health and wellbeing. Put it differently, *feminist emotion* emerged in the process of learning and knowledge related processes. The unequivocal sign is that since the very beginning of N-HbM actions an affective attunement to the emotional traces that gender experiences triggered at the individual or community level occurred and was the means to empowerment; empowerment referred to by Alonso as "reconstruction" of the inner possibilities or capabilities of each woman for becoming subjects of knowledge about experience, and agents of knowledge production about program implementation.

Araceli Alonso explains that the preference for family-ran water-tank installation over the construction of a community-ran well on the part of the local women was due to a desire to preserve the strong sense of sorority that had emerged among the women from different villages. This preference is a good example of how effective the affective communication and affective ties nurtured by N-HbM are even for the logistics of intervention. The local women unquestionably perceived that control and command over prospective problems related to water management would be settled more efficiently by operating at the micro-level (family units) as opposed to at a larger communitarian level, and through alliance rather than vigilance.

It is possible to talk about empowerment as an internal process, something that took place within the individual, but if empowerment is only discussed within the conceptual parameters of symbolic individual well defined contours, it is not possible to reach a satisfying explanation of the type of feminist agency that came up and was cemented through the programs. The fact that affect was so fruitful is related to the process of women's attunement to their own affect but also to that of other women. A rebellious component of affect, namely *feminist emotion*—pure primary agency—was actively involved in how gender was transcended as a limiting conditioner that produced multiple negative affective effects in emotionality. Harsh living circumstances and gender discrimination are at the root of disempowerment; but free circulating affect, collective affective communication that transcended the individual, was essential for the women in Lunga Lunga to begin feeling that they could overcome hardship. Thus, N-HbM programs' first level of effective work had much more to do with fostering venues through which women regained ownership and a sense of authorship towards their own experiential knowledge through affect, than with providing the means to acquire diverse types of new knowledge, skills, or capabilities. It is, in fact, circulating affective knowledge on gender discrimination that makes the difference.

### *Joy*

How can affectively induced knowledge be organized and channeled for it to become a forceful indisputable element for individual and collective transformation? What are the internal processes that a person, a family, a group, a community may go through when a renovated empowered relationship to knowledge takes root? Some of the answers to these intricate questions may be deduced from my comments to another episode commented by Alonso: the Nikumbuke Women's excursion to Diane Beach. In my view,, this episode holds a special value for understanding another forceful element of the HbAM model: Joy.

A water tank leads to more time to think, more time for discussion and debate, opportunities for girls' education, more time and eagerness to play. Play leads to productive thinking and learning, more positive attitudes for discussion and debates, improved wellbeing. Araceli Alonso uses Performative Theory to explain the bodily communication that sprouted everywhere in very productive ways as N-HbM programs unfolded and progressed. I am particularly taken by her narration of the beach scene and scenario as a turning point at the equator of the programs. Let us recall that within N-HbM programs, a free-time leisure activity is often planned as an integral part of the health promoters training. The group is usually taken to the closest beach, Diane Beach, for expansion, for fun. Perhaps, in addition to Performance Theory, the event at Diane Beach can best be explained through the concept of autonomous affect, as posed by affect theorists. According to the central claim of Affect Theory, affect exists anywhere, anytime, beyond and in spite of the subject and the social. Although I agree with this claim in general terms, I want to call attention to what may occur <u>before</u> affect becomes the protagonist. Which are, intentionally or unintentionally created, the conditions for affect to circulate and be likely to "surpass" the individual and collective subject, to forcefully shape the bodily interactions of the bodies, and mold the space where they move? In relation to the Diane Beach episode narrated by Alonso, the question also is why positive affect emerged the way it did, autonomously, in Ukunda.

Let me begin by suggesting that joy and playfulness are the result and the means, the "during" and the "after," not the precondition to wellbeing. It is clear to me that the kind of empowerment that had been taking place over the years before the beach episode allowed the women of the group to intensely rejoice the moment, in-as-much as they previously found it reassuring to share their sorrows and worries with each other during the initial health camps, follow-up training workshops and theater performance sessions. I am referring to the empowerment that originates in affect and specifically, in gendered affect, that was so productively nurtured.

The scene of the never-before visited beach or never seen ocean by the people who live only fifteen kilometers away recalls an appropriation and even liberation of a historical past of colonization. This assertion becomes more undisputable when one travels to this area. The ocean can be smelled but not seen from Lunga Lunga. The ocean has a sort of selective absence-presence, for it can only be imagined by those who have previously had the privilege to see it closely, in Ukunda or elsewhere. As a foreign outsider who often spends time by the sea in my home country, I was certainly able to smell and imagine it, even if I did not have the chance to go near it while visiting Lunga Lunga. I could envision what some parts of the coast line may look like when I saw other white people who had sporadically left their luxurious hotels for a brief hang out into "unsafe territory" inhabited by the local people. I saw a white man and a woman coquettishly showing off their power over local transgender gigolos as they shared a beer and some food with them. This disturbing sight of neocolonial dynamics was brought up into my imaginary of the nearby ocean and shaped my interpretation of Araceli Alonso's powerful narration of the beach episode. To Western standards it is almost inconceivable that such a close, beautiful and powerful physical domain is so utterly absent from the local people's lives; it is only when one has a sense of the historical past of colonization and slavery trade, and is aware of contemporary global power dynamics, that the symbolic meaning embedded in simple facts like the absence of fresh fish in most local people's diet becomes amenable to interpretation.

The HbAM model is about rural development of very isolated areas. This means that it is about people whose lives are consumed by daily struggles for survival. Enjoying the ocean is partly "forbidden" by privatization of a great deal of the coast line as well as a time-consuming and expensive luxury that is largely incompatible with survival struggles. Fifteen kilometers are not the same fifteen kilometers for everybody there. Araceli Alonso's powerful narration of the beach episodes recalls how exceptional the beach excursion was for the group. Picking up a moto-taxi or buying a ticket for a ride on a minibus to cover the distance may simply mean depriving your own family of food for a whole month; it may also mean, as it is the case of people who live in a village called Maasailand, walking non-stop for endless hours.

Even if the Diane Beach episode cannot just be interpreted away from its past and situated historicity, the importance of the historical background that led to the joyful shared moment at the beach is directly and inevitably linked to the fact that previous present instances were enacted as a-historical. What I mean by this is that during the comprehensive work carried out by N-HbM prior to the episode and guided by the *Umoja* approach, the local participants had liberated themselves temporarily from the weight of their own historicity, from their socio-cultural baggage that they are unfairly meant to carry and its resulting affective heaviness.

Somehow, a fostered sense of a-historical immediate past was a precondition for joy to emerge and was promoted through the several formal and informal interactions that consistently nurtured trust and solidarity.

In Araceli Alonso's ethnographic narration, the beach episode really begins before the journey, prior to motion and arrival at the beach. At the Nikumbuke Health Center; when referring to the session in which the group tried on bathing suits for the excursion, she states: "We lost any former trait of identity as we unleashed the power of unity, the plenitude of oneness." Free circulating positive affect jointed all the bodies in their conquest of new spatial sensorial experiences: The half-naked bodies mingled and laughed in a simulated theatrical dressing room; their costume-like suits, ready for the excursion to come, were like the passport for a transitory passage to liberation from sorrow and hardship. The spontaneous erasure of boundaries, the annulation of identity filters merged with the excitement and joyful moment to anticipate and pre-set the atmosphere for an Arcadian-like moment at the beach to come; a moment full of sensorial elements: the sun, the salty water, the warmth of the sand, the caressing air. At the beach episode narrated by Araceli Alonso, hierarchies were totally blurred amidst participants, facilitators, students, local coordinators, the doctor, the dentist, the nurse, and also the environment itself. Some of the international facilitators were the only ones to have seen the ocean before; but they found themselves completely drawn into the joyful energy of the first-time ocean-watchers and the activity itself, to the point that their distinctiveness disappeared in the collective body of the group. All participants were entangled in the affective threads that emanated from the women and men of Lunga Lunga and the other villages, rejoicing in a newly owned space and time.

Araceli Alonso's appreciation that her own situated and culturally mediated learnt knowledge at first became an obstacle to deeply understand joyful human behavior adds an important additional twist to the above observations. There is also much to say about the momentary suspension of historicity as it applies to the baggage of culture that might have tainted the international facilitators' knowledge and experience at the beach. Their aprioristic perceptions about gender and ethnic dynamics were utterly questioned by the very occurrences that took place at the beach, both as spectators and as participants. Bodily affect took over, once more. The relevance of experiential knowledge surpassed that of any other kind of knowledge and freed everybody equally from pre-set hierarchies of subjugating ethnic and other type of identity differences such as illness, pain, personal circumstances, bodily conditions, disabilities, and so on. Facilitators abandoned themselves to positive affect flow in the body, amidst other bodies, just like the local participants did.

No doubt that the work carried out previously by all participants and facilitators led to the moment at Diane Beach. The spontaneous avoidance of the barriers of historicity and structural power dynamics was possible thanks to N-HbM's own history of an *Umoja* kind of intervention in Lunga Lunga that had taken place for three years up to this point. By the time play and joy developed at the beach episode, several levels of intervention had taken place already through educational actions and basic-needs coverage: a health promoters training program, several health promotion campaigns, health camps, health parties carried out by the trained health promoters, theater performances for prevention campaigns, literacy classes, the inauguration of a permanent health post and a sewing training school, a Moringa Tree plantation and cooperative, as well as diverse service-oriented actions such as the installation of water tanks, distribution of mosquito nets, and health assistance through a mobile unit. As Araceli Alonso describes it, a cascade effect of various intervention actions led to joy and play to take over the way it did at the beach; just like a water tank installation at Mama Margret's home led to her daughters' attendance at school, unprecedented solidarity for water-sharing amidst neighbors of different ethnicities, her own request to be officially trained by the government as a health worker, and several communities requesting a women's soccer team and league; just like the mixed ethnically hybrid space of the Moringa cooperative contributed to the erasure of conflict and cohabiting difficulties and led to the local women's request of another joyful long-lasting initiative of a bodily nature: the Soccer League.

Araceli Alonso claims that the capability referred to as "Play" by Martha C. Nussbaum sprouted when and because other capabilities had been fostered too through multiple actions guided by the *Umoja* approach. Nevertheless, in order to fully understand its relevance in relation to the particular way N-HbM programs unfolded, it is important to pay close attention to the affective processes that pointed the way to the event and shaped why and how it all happened, as well as its outcome (Nussbaum 2011). Put differently, paying attention to affective processes would explain why one action was ingrained unstoppably on the other, among other things, because affect is contagious, as neuroscientists have demonstrated (Seyfert 2012; Brennan 2006). The contagious effect of positive affect and gender-related rebellious affect molded by *feminist emotion* empowered local women, enhanced women's sense of unity and their ownership over all the actions and programs, and its transforming effect expanded from one community to the other. Furthermore, affect took the shape of awareness of gender discrimination and thus gave rise to leadership and even advocacy initiatives for the sake of gender equality.

The trip towards the beach is an embodied journey itself. New bodily interactions began on the road. It was the very first time that the group and facilitators sat together as just friends. In the mini-van, shoulder-to-shoulder, they shared laughter; also, fear of stopping at a terrorist threatened commercial area; pleasure too, when tasting the exotic white people's food. Metaphorically, the road is part of another journey that started much earlier at the initial health camps. Yet, the road experience was marked by the ease and naturalness of a "first time" event. A natural rupture with all sorts of hierarchies took place and allowed self-discovery processes among the participants as someone other than the usual self in-as-much-as discovery of the "other(s)" (Bruns 2000). Besides the group hierarchies—between diverse ethnic individuals, between beneficiaries and facilitators, students and Alonso, nurse and doctor, and so on—other unspoken hierarchies were also surpassed smoothly, thanks to the positive affect that freely circulated: local geographical boundaries between the rural and the urban, the wealthy and the poor, the white or whiter and the dark-skinned, the disabled and non-disabled, the elder and the young, men and women, inner-tribal divisions, etc.

Important information is to be extracted from sensory engagements; "bodily judgements" may contain a significant epistemological value (Waitt, Ryan and Farbotko 2014: 288). A concrete working agenda was not preset nor planned for the excursion to Diane Beach. In fact, the absence of such an agenda was precisely what allowed the bodies to naturally produce transgressive meaning about surpassing the social through embodied engagement. The non-systematization of a previous work plan facilitated that a playful activity became just this: A playful sensorial experience of diverse bodily affective emotional responses. But the playful, joyful, spontaneous bodily nature of the Diane Beach episode can be said to have deep political relevance as a peace-building event for it entailed the total suspension of ethnic, religious, cultural, age, racial, educational, gender boundaries. As Araceli Alonso recalls, at the beach, all hierarchies and identity barriers disappeared: Women became girls, girls acted like the rest of the women; Muslim women took off their head veils; each freely chose a type of bathing attire; all bodies partly uncovered and marked by self-chosen specific costumes worn for the first time; men and women enjoying the moment as equals; the Maasai—a historically highly discriminated against ethnic group—wearing their costumes into the water and enjoying themselves with the rest of the group. Bodies exposed to each other, imperfect and vulnerable, showing the scars of life and history but performing the enactment of a temporary erasure of their marks as differential obstacles for a shared humanity.

My grasp of the importance of this joyful event in the context of the community life transformation that had been taking place since 2009 as a result of N-HbM intervention, was initially just based on Araceli Alonso's narration and filtered through my own intellectual preferences for feminist theory and affect theory. However, after a recent visit to Lunga Lunga and surroundings, I can only say that my incipient conclusions found strong evidence in real life. While I was in the region, I witnessed and participated in other moments of joyful collective sharing that—I believe—were also clear enactments of the fruitful power of positive and rebellious affect, specifically, *feminist emotion*. It is impossible to measure the extent, scope, characteristics, details, variations of such affective power and the emotional processes that it originated throughout the years, but it is certainly feasible to feel the intensity of its impact in the warmth of hand-shaking, the facial expressions or momentary laughter during brief personal encounters. One cannot be insensitive to the instant dilutions of the marks or shadows of hardship on the facial skin and the eyes of many local women, when they merge into an explosive guffaw, as they watched us, visitors, clumsily trying to imitate their carefully rehearsed dance steps. But, somehow, I am certain that the scars and shadows were deeper and more obscure some years ago, prior to the N-HbM programs, and that, among many other things that have already been mentioned and others that have not, collective enjoyment truly helped to dilute those scars and shadows.

Referring back to the beach episode, one can state that it was the shared vulnerability of the bodies that simultaneously brought them all together and liberated them from each other, as well as from the burden of their embodied existence in the social. In other activities of N-HbM, expressions of sorrow overflew the individual—i.e. what occurred during the gender-based-violence health promoters training workshop and productively contributed to prompt stronger affective alliances; at the beach episode, it was the momentary joy of experiencing liberation from time and spatial constraints what fostered a strong sense of complicity among the members of the group. No wonder why Araceli Alonso states that there is no way back after Diane Beach. The effect of such complicity triggered by the bodily positive affective experience expands much farther than the sole event of a day excursion at the beach. In my view, the extended relevance of the event has much to do with the fact that it fostered a living-in-the-moment existence; leaving everything on hold, enjoying the right to simply rejoice with oneself and one-another "right here right now"; the normative construction of a balance between reason and emotions set aside (Harkin 2003: 266). And the positive effect of such joyful affective occurrences has a long-lasting effect in emotionality, as neuroscientists would argue, because the human brain is highly malleable and subject to the impact—positive or negative—of experience (Davidson and Bruce S. McEwen 2012).

As I see it, the epistemological interpretative value of the Diane Beach episode in the context of N-HbM comprehensive approach is enormous: The joyful present instance figuratively replaced the shadows and scars of ongoing struggles with illness, poverty, violence, to the point that it created the momentary illusion of having overcome a painful immediate past. In turn, the immediate past was perceived, strongly, as shared memory, and as a result, the former illusory perception as a collective victory. Embodied political agency sprouted through the powerful healing experience of positive affect; positive affect prompted a new and strong collective historical narrative. In other words, shared embodied joy in the present time created a strong awareness of the shared social, negative and positive in the past. Thus, the Diane

Beach episode is a cornerstone in the pathway of individual and community empowerment that was being nurtured through N-HbM multi-leveled holistic actions and programs. It is currently widely accepted that together with many other factors, negative or positive affect and emotional processes play a direct cause-effect role in inducing illness or healthy conditions (Davidson 2012; Coe 2015; Seeman 2015). Also, the fact is that, when dealing with maternal health, such effect may expand to the child, as is the case of lactating babies (Tapias 2006). Thus, whether symbolically or literally, physically or psychologically, individually or collectively, there is a highly beneficial healing power to play and joy because they trigger positive affect; thus, they are a necessary component to be incorporated in health and wellbeing development programs.

> Joy is essential to HbAM and it can be prompted by play through any kind of related actions.

The diverse affective "bodily discourses" uttered playfully and linguistically articulated through shared experiential knowledge recalling instances complement each other. Various activities fostered by N-HbM—the health camps, theater performances, workshops, health promoters training and health parties, informal discussions at the Moringa Tree cooperative establishment, and so on, contributed to creating a cascade effect of the programs. I would say that one activity, one action, one program, could not be without the other, and that any one's transformative power would be diminished or highly unfruitful if fostered in isolation.

Another key to the *Umoja* approach and N-HbM operative means is:

> A naturally unfolding mechanism of all the initiatives within its comprehensive approach. Actions to be taken are decided upon request by the local women through collective

approval, and are shaped and developed entirely by the communities.

Araceli Alonso explains how the initial concerns about maternal and reproductive health soon yielded to many other, much more general, questions about the body and wellbeing at large. N-HbM avoided falling into an ethnocentric view of health and illness through dialogue, listening, question-answer strategies in which the very local women provided the fundamental answers and solutions. It was precisely by "allowing" women to reclaim answers for many diverse questions that facilitators became aware of their own limitations for intervention, as I have explained in the previous section entitled 'Knowledge'. While the active discursive engagement or ownership of discourse on the part of the women from the communities who seek information and knowledge about their bodies and wellbeing, was precisely what literally triggered the unfolding of all the N-HbM programs, it was joy that kept it all together and made it all sustainable. Medical services intervention programs, the health promoters training, the installation of water-tanks, the creation of a Moringa Tree cooperative, the Soccer League, the Sawing School, etc. enacted with much energy and devotion by the "direct beneficiaries," the local women, constitute the comprehensive approach to health as wellbeing that I have analyzed. But the HbAM model is not just about a series of programs, actions or even unique operating mechanisms; it is mainly about the enhancement of knowledge and joy as means to better envision the intimate and intricate connection that exist between diverse aspects of life and our own sense of a desired wellbeing.

## Self-Reflection

As I have stated in the previous sections, most of my inter-pretative essay was written as informed by several years of reflection over what I had heard, read, or seen via indirect sources. However, in December of 2016, I had the chance to visit Lunga Lunga and the other nearby village where the programs are being implemented. I traveled with Araceli Alonso, and met some of the women that I had been writing and thinking about from the distance. My only work plan was to observe, see, listen, feel, and to informally interview the two main leaders: the general local coordinator, Bendettah Thomas, and the nurse, Josephine Martin, who weekly travels by motorbike to each village to provide basic health assistance and offer general health literacy classes to the local women. I had prepared a long set of questions to guide me through these interviews but the questions would ultimately be totally useless. The clairvoyance of the interviewees and the blatant evidence derived from my own affective experience of meeting the local women obliterated the rational that went into the interview planning.

Throughout my short visit, I tried to control my emotional processes to remain in an intellectual mind-framework about HbAM by scrutinizing myself and everybody through many questions about the N-HbM programs and actions. Such inquisi-tiveness became a bit exhausting and even uncomfortable for myself and my colleague. Upon my return home, the emotional sensations stood out intensely above all to provide me with clairvoyance for my analysis. I realized that there was a profound contradiction between the content of my writing about affect as a ubiquitous force whose transformative power often passes unnoticed, and the persistent nature of the queries during my visit. While I was explaining why and how the erasure of hierar-chies, specifically, the hierarchies of knowledge, are a core guiding element of the HbAM model, I clung to my condition as a distant academic observer and tried to make of it the guiding principle for my observations and sensations on the spot. Ironically—and fortunately—such realization later allowed me to further claim that emotionality is a crucial analytical dimension of the model.

Everywhere we went while I was in the region, the Nikumbuke Women had prepared a welcoming celebration for us that included singing, dancing and lots of gifts, hugs, laughter. Tears kept coming to my eyes as I watched them dancing for us; among other things, I knew I did not deserve it all; unlike Araceli Alonso, I had done nothing for them yet. I felt inadequate to receive such love, gratitude and generosity. Thus, I continued spinning up my mind instead of just staying with the flow of the moment and learning from it through emotionality in affect. Later, I understood that to fully experience the forceful effect of affect in such context was not only to abandon control of myself and my intellectual abilities, but also to confront reflections about the limits of scientific knowledge itself. I was not intellectually ready for it by then; today, I have come to accept that life is much more complex and mysterious than the explanations we can provide of it. My quest for answers during my visit was in fact what left my incapacity to answer them exposed to myself. My perception of the programs was situated in my own thoughts as well as in my personal and professional backgrounds and scientific knowledge but, somehow, I was crudely confronted with the impossibility of capturing the nuances and specificities of the others' situated realities. As an outsider, I lacked authority to understand the lives of the women that I met; I lacked authority over my own affect and emotional processes that were triggered by the encounters with them. I was owned in/by affect. The Nikumbuke Women neutral-ized me as an observer completely; a role that I had previously imagined and experienced as power.

Literally, the musical narrations to welcome us, visitors, in every village, in a language that I could not understand—Swahili—

symbolized what the local women were teaching me: The inextricable impotence of words and concepts to explain the concreteness and fineness of their lives and their emotionality; including, the deep transformation their lives and selves were undergoing with N-HbM programs and actions. Bendettah Thomas translated for me some of the lyrics of the greeting songs. Thanking Araceli Alonso was a predominant theme, but they also thanked me for visiting them, for being Alonso's guest and friend. In addition, their singing was about what they wanted to do next; it was a musical narration of their own planning agenda: They wanted a secondary school in Jirani, more water-tanks in Maasailand, additional training in first-aid basics in Lunga Lunga and Perani, etc. What they asked from us was just guidance, support and some help, for instance, in providing the training for them. The obscene intrusiveness of my intellectual process about them and the N-HbM programs seemed pointless when confronted with these sang instances of their desired wellbeing. But my own experiential emotional knowledge of their celebratory welcomes kept triggering new questions. Ultimately, I was confronted with the realization that it was futile to keep at seeking certain answers. Life is simpler and has many profound layers that we are unable to discern rationally. Josephine Matini's illuminating answer to my question about what N-HbM was for her forcefully sums it all: "Happiness for seeing other women happy."

Meaning is physical. Until meaning is not realized through physical encounters it does not exist completely. We must accept that we are lost in knowledge. In fact, accepting this is the only way to crack open a tiny window to observe and understand unpredictable meaning through physicality and by incorporating physicality into intellectual processes. Direct experiential knowledge of reality is what makes our thinking somehow meaningless; and yet our knowledge is always meaningful because it is ruled by affect. We never know completely because knowing is a permanent process of discovery that is always enhanced through the subtleties of our own living experiences in/and/through the living of others, also deeply touched by affect. We are meant to believe that we must know; that it is our duty to know when, in fact, the desire to know is just a desperate attempt at not surrendering, abandoning ourselves to physicality.

Can meaning be felt? Physicality cannot be thought about or analyze completely. Thinking is avoiding the physicality of experience and experiencing the abyss of an absent venue towards it. Our only chance to approach the life of others in such a way that we may perceive traces of their complexity, needs and wishes is to depart from what I would call *a physical conviction* about the complementary nature of knowledge. Different communities and religions, diverse ethnic groups and individuals observe each other and themselves, learn from each other, and are transformed by the many regular encounters that are being fostered by the local coordinator, the nurse, and Araceli Alonso. After briefly visiting Lunga Lunga and some of the surrounding villages, after thoroughly thinking through the information that Araceli Alonso and others have generously shared with me, I firmly believe that the marvels that are taking place in Lunga Lunga and surroundings very much derive from the natural erasure of the boundaries and hierarchies of knowledge. Such erasure is fueled by the promotion of joy, which originates positive affect and facilitates its prompting to the surface, its circulation and its productive flourishing into wellbeing and peace.

Our resistance to the power of affect as knowing is due to our fear of the utter elimination of referential hierarchies in the unavoidable materiality of experience. Knowers, as outside observers, are just one more shifting element in the processes of living of all other living creatures and material elements. Dust and heat, water and sun, mosquitos and sweat, scratchy bushes, smell, music, smog of motorbikes, tears and laughter, suspicious or grateful eyes, the warmth of the hands, and so on, all of it, simultaneously, remind us of our overwhelming physical proximity to knowing and the impenetrability of what we want to know. We all belong to an endless unknown terrain and must not trap ourselves or others in our thoughts. Life will expand the limits of our individuality without despotic mechanisms, only if we remain open to the physicality of meaning. As we continue to avoid vulnerability and impotence and stay put to the illusion of knowing—which is nothing other than holding on to difference as privilege—that which we want to know will escape further and further. The arrogance of the thinking self is exposed on a fragile mirror always about to be violently broken by the experiential affective knowledge of others, their lives, their suffering and joy, their strategies for living, their daily transformations. Our realization that "they" elude our meaning-making, as intensely as they seek health, wellbeing, and peace, and run away from death through love, is the final answer.

Trans-feminist theorists like Susan Stryker make use of the prefix "trans" to place the spotlight onto the passageways of *connection* and *circulation* between the macro- and the micro-political that trouble all identity recognitions including nation and citizenship, and that span beyond identity and structures (Jardine 2010: 71-72). This definition of "trans" as a crosscutting of categories where ambivalence allows for a particular productive kind of connection and circulation of diverse levels of reality is particularly relevant to my analysis of the HbAM model regarding the following:

1. The effectiveness of its comprehensive transdisciplinarity;
2. The circularity of the activities: Planning and affect circulation;
3. The importance of the micro in prompting macro-changes in the communities;
4. The epistemological relevance of the micro- in the context of a feminist interpretation of the supra-structural subversive meaning that N-HbM programs entail as they foster social change.

I believe that the unstoppable cascade effect of the process of wellbeing and peace-building that is going on in Lunga Lunga area, as a result of the work described in this book, spins beyond the fragility of the social coexistence of the region, where religious fundamentalist groups like Al-Shabab are planting the seeds of hatred. Women are empowered and united; they are threaded by affect and *feminist emotion*, touched by a no-return gender-based rebellious component that is being channeled into collective empowerment, fueled by their resilience power as humans. Even if social conflict may not be avoided in the future, the collective transformation that women are leading is, no doubt, deeper and more powerful than any outside disturbing factor. As Araceli Alonso once told me: "the Nikumbuke Women will rise and stay together, if necessary, for a long long time."

# BIOGRAPHIES

## Araceli Alonso

Dr. Alonso is an Associate Faculty at the University of Wisconsin-Madison in the Department of Gender and Women's Studies, the School of Human Ecology, and the School of Medicine and Public Health, where she teaches classes on women's health and women's rights. Alonso holds a Nursing degree, a Bachelors degree in History, a Master of Science, a Master of Arts, and a Ph.D. in Medical Anthropology. Dr. Alonso is also co-founder and co-director of the University of Wisconsin-Madison UNESCO Chair on Gender, Wellbeing and Culture of Peace. She is the author of the internationally acclaimed *Out of Havana: Memoirs of Ordinary Life in Cuba*. Dr. Alonso received two of the world's most prestigious awards—the United Nations Public Service Award and the Jefferson Award for Public Service for her women's health initiative *Nikumbuke-Health by Motorbike* (N-HbM). Alonso is also the Director for Gender, Health and Clinical Practice of the University of Wisconsin's research-to-action and local-to-global 4W-STREETS Initiative (Social Transformation to End the Exploitation and Trafficking for Sex). Alonso's research expertise is on women's global health and human rights. In 2015 Dr. Alonso was named one of the 100 most influential women world leaders in Global Health.

aalonso@wisc.edu
http://unesco.gws.wisc.edu
healthbymotorbike.wix.com/healthbymotorbike

## Teresa Langle de Paz

Dr. Langle de Paz is co-founder and co-director of the UNESCO Chair on Gender, Wellbeing and Culture of Peace in the Department of Gender and Women's Studies at the University of Wisconsin, Madison (USA) (www.unesco.gws.wisc.edu). She is currently the director of Phare Nador at the Foundation Women for Africa in Spain (www.mujeresporafrica.es), an institution devoted to the promotion of African women's leadership and empowerment, where she is also a member of the Advisory Board. She is a member of the Executive Council of various research institutes at Autonomous University and Complutense University of Madrid, Spain. She has a Doctorate in Philosophy from Brown University and has been a professor of Early Modern Spanish Literature and Feminist Theory at Lawrence University and the University of Houston in the US and at Complutense University, International Menéndez Pelayo University, and Jaume I University in Spain. She has published on Early Modern feminism and Feminist Theory in top scientific journals, has edited various books on diverse feminist topics, and is the author of two monographic books on feminist theory entitled *La urgencia de vivir. Teoría feminista de las emociones* (Barcelona: Anthropos, 2018)— Urgent Living. Feminist Theory of Emotions—and *La rebelión sigilosa. El poder transformador de la* emoción feminista (Col. Akademia. Barcelona: Icaria, 2011)—The Stealthy Rebellion. The Transformational Power of *Feminist Emotion.*

langledepaz@wisc.edu
http://unesco.gws.wisc.edu
tlangledepaz@mujeresporafrica.es

# BIBLIOGRAPHY

## PART I. ETHNOGRAPHY

Boal, Augusto (1979). *Teatro do oprimido e outras poéticas políticas*, Rio de Janeiro: Civilização Brasileira.

Boal, Augusto (1995). *The Rainbow of Desire: The Boal Method of Theatre and Therapy*, London: Routledge.

Estrella, Maria Corazón P. et al. (2000). "A Double-blind, Randomized Controlled Trial on the use of *Malunggay (Moringa Oleifera)* for Augmentation of the Volume of Breastmilk among Non-nursing Mothers of Preterm Infants." *Philippine Journal of Pediatrics*, 49 (1): 3-6.

Food and Agriculture Organization of the United Nations (FAO) (1992). "Forest, Trees and Food." Available from: http://www.fao.org/docrep/006/u5620e /U5620E00.HTM

Freire, Paulo (1970). *Pedagogy of the Oppressed*. New York: Herder and Herder.

Hornby, Charles (2012). *Kenya: A History Since Independence*. I.B. London: Tauris & Co Ltd.

Kenya National Bureau of Statistics and ICF International. (2016). *National Malaria Control Programme. Kenya Malaria Indicator Survey 2015*. Nairobi, Kenya, and Rockville, Maryland, USA.

Kenya National Bureau of Statistics (KNBS) (2013). *Exploring Kenya's Inequality, Pulling Apart or Pooling Together? Kwale County.*

Kenya National Bureau of Statistics (KNBS) (2010). *2009 Population and Housing Census Results*, Kenya.

Lederach, John Paul (2005). *The Moral Imagination: The Art and Soul of Building Peace*. New York: Oxford University Press.

Maathai, Wangari (2010). *Replenishing the Earth: Spiritual Values for Healing Ourselves and the World*. New York: Random House Inc.

Marcu, Monica (2013). *Miracle Tree*. Utah: Sound Concepts.

Martínez Guzmán, Vicent (2005)., *Podemos hacer las paces: reflexiones éticas tras el 11-S y el 11-M*. Colección Ética Aplicada, Sevilla: Publidisa.

Ministry of Lands Department of Physical Planning (MLDPP), and United Nations Centre for Regional Development (2011). *Kwale District and Mombasa Mainland South Regional Physical Development Plan 2014-2034*, Nairobi.

Martha Nussbaum (2000). *Women and Human Development: The Capabilities Approach.* New York: Cambridge University Press.

Ndubuaka, U.M. et at. (2014). "Yield characteristics of *Moringa oleifera* Across Different Ecologies in Nigeria as an Index of its Adaptation to Climate Change." *Sustainable Agriculture Research*, 3 (1): 95-100.

Ole Simel, Joseph (2004). "The Century-long Displacement and Dispossession of the Maasai in Kenya." *Indigenous Affairs*, 04/2004: 42-46.

Olol-Dapash, Meitamei (2001). "Maasai Autonomy and Sovereignty in Kenya and Tanzania." *Cultural Survival Quarterly*, 25 (1), Available from:
http://www.culturalsurvival.org/ourpublications/csq/
article/maasai-autonomy-and-sovereignty-kenya-and-tanzania

Sloman, Annie (2011). *Using participatory theatre in international community development.* Community Development Journal: Oxford University Press and, January 27.

Sommer, Doris (2014). *The Work of Art in the World: Civic Agency and Public Humanities.* Duke University Press.

Steketee, Richar W.; Bernard L. Nahlen, Monica E. Parise, and Clara Menendez (2001). "The Burden of Malaria in Pregnancy in Malaria-Endemic Areas." in *The Intolerable Burden of Malaria: A New Look at the Numbers.* Supplement to Volume 64(1) of the *American Journal of Tropical Medicine and Hygiene* (Breman JG, Egan A, Keusch GT, ed,), Northbrook (IL): American Society of Tropical Medicine and Hygiene.

Van Vark, Casper (2013). "Improving Access to Services for Women in Agriculture." *The Guardian,* Available from:
http://www.theguardian.com/global-development

## PART II. PHILOSOPHY AND THEORY

Ahmed, Sara (2010). "Happy Objects." In *The Affect Theory Reader*, ed. Melissa Gregg and Gregory J. Seigworth. Durham, N.C.: Duke University Press.

—. (2012). "Whiteness and the General Will: Diversity Work as Willful Work." *PhiloSOPHIA* 2 (1): 1–20.

Anderson, Ben (2010). Modulating the Excess of Affect: Morale in a State of "Total War." In *The Affect Theory Reader*, ed. Melissa Gregg and Gregory J. Seigworth. Durham, N.C.: Duke University Press.

Brennan, Teresa (2004). *The Transmission of Affect*. Ithaca, N.Y.: Cornell University Press.

Bruns, John (2000). "Laughter in the Aisles: Affect and Power in Contemporary Theoretical and Cultural Discourse." *Studies in American Humor*. Special Issue: *Humor and Ethnicity in the Americas* 3 (7): 5-23.

Burkitt, Ian (2012). "Emotional Reflexivity: Feeling, Emotion and Imagination in Reflexive Dialogues." *Sociology*, 46 (3): 458-472.

Cockburn, Cynthia (2007). *From Where We Stand. War, Women's Activism and Feminist Analysis*. London: Zed Books.

Coe L., Christopher y Gabriele R. Lubach. (2015). "Social Context and Other Psychological Influences on Development of Immunity." In Carol D. Ryff y Burton H. Singer (eds). *Emotion, Social Relations and Health*. 243-261

Davidson, Richard J. (2012). *The Emotional Life of Your Brain: How Its Unique Patterns Affect the Way You Think, Feel, and Live—and How You Can Change Them*. New York: Plume.

Davidson, Richard J., and Bruce S. McEwen (2012). Social Influences on Neuroplasticity: Stress and Interventions to Promote Well-Being. *Nature Neuroscience* 15 (5): 689–95.

Denzin, Norman K. and Michael D. Giardina, eds. (2010). *Qualitative Inquiry and Human Rights*. California: Left Coast Press. California.

Denzin, Norman K. (2009). *On Understanding Emotion*. New Brunswick, N.J.: Transaction Publishers.

Foucault, Michael (1988). "Technologies of the Self." In L. Martin, H. Gutman and P. Hutton, eds. *Technologies of the Self: A Seminar with Michel Foucault*. Tavistock: London, 16–49.

Greenberg, Leslie (2008). "Emotion and Cognition in Psychotherapy: The Transforming Power of Affect." *Canadian Psychology* 49 (1): 49-59.

Harding, Sandra (1993). "Rethinking Standpoint Epistemology: What Is Strong Objectivity?" In *Feminist Epistemologies*, ed. Linda Alcoff and Elizabeth Potter. London: Routledge.

Harkin, Michael E. (2003). "Feeling and Thinking in Memory and Forgetting: Towards an Ethnohistory of the Emotions." *Ethnohistory* 50 (2): 261-284.

Harris, Oliver J. T. and Tim Flohr Sorensen (2010). "Rethinking Emotion and Material Culture." *Archaeological Dialogues* 17 (2): 145-163.

Hemmings, Clare (2012). "Affective Solidarity: Feminist Reflexivity and Political Transformation." *Feminist Theory* 13 (2): 147–61.

Jaggar, Alison M. (1989). "Love and knowledge: Emotion in Feminist Epistemology." *Inquiry: An Interdisciplinary Journal of Philosophy* 32 (2): 151–76.

Jardine, Alice (2010). "What Feminism?" *French Politics, Culture & Society* 28 (2): 66-74.

Langle de Paz, Teresa. (2018). *La urgencia de vivir. Teoría feminista de las emociones* (Urgent Living. A Feminist Theory of Emotions). Barcelona: Anthropos.

—. (2016). "A Golden Lever for Politics: *Feminist Emotion* and Women's Agency." *Hypatia* 31 (1): 187-203.

—. (2010). *La rebelion sigilosa: El poder transformador de la* emoción feminista. Madrid: Icaria.

Lawler, Edward J. and Shane R. Thye (1999). "Bringing Emotions into Social Exchange Theory." *Annual Review of Sociology,* 25: 217-244.

Lingis, Alphonso (2010). "Emanations." *Parallax* 16 (2): 12–19.

Mackenzie, Catriona (2000). "Imagining Oneself Otherwise." In *Relational Autonomy: Feminist Perspectives on Autonomy, Agency, and the Social Self,* ed. Catriona Mackenzie and Natalie Stoljar. Oxford: Oxford University Press.

Massumi, Brian (1995). "The Autonomy of Affect." *Cultural Critique* 31 (II): 83–109.

—. (2010). "Ontology of Threat." In *The Affect Theory Reader,* ed. Melissa Gregg and Gregory J. Seigworth. Durham, N.C.: Duke University Press.

Nussbaum, Martha C. (2011). *Creating Capabilities: The Human Development Approach.* Cambridge, Mass.: Harvard University Press.

—. (2000). *Women and Human Development. The Capabilities Approach.* Cambridge: Cambridge University Press.

Ryff, Carol D. y Burton H. Singer. (Eds). (2015). *Emotion, Social Relations and Health.* Oxford: Oxford University Press.

Seeman, Teresa E. (2015). "How Do Others Get under Our Skin? Social Relationships and Health." In Carol D. Ryff (ed). *Emotion, Social Relations and Health.* Oxford: Oxford University Press. 189-209

Seyfert, Robert. (2012). "Beyond Personal Feelings and Collective Emotions: Toward a Theory of Social Affect." *Theory, Culture and Society.* 29(6): 27-46.

Sen, Amartya K. (1999). *Development as Freedom*. Oxford: Oxford University Press.

Tapias, María. (2006). "Emotions and the Intergenerational Embodiment of Social Suffering in Rural Bolivia." *Medical Anthropology Quarterly*, 20(3): 399-415.

Waitt, Gordon, Ella Ryan and Carol Farbotko (2014). "A Visceral Politics of Sound." *Antipode*, 46 (1): 283-300.

Wetherell, Margaret. (2012). *Affect and Emotion. A New Social Science Understanding*. London: Sage Publications.

## DEEP EDUCATION PRESS
## SCIENTIFIC BOARD MEMBERS

Dr. Stephanie Fonvielle, Associate Professor, Teacher Education University Institute, University of Aix-Marseille, France

Dr. Elliot Gaines, Professor, Wright State University, President Semiotic Society of America, International Communicology Institute, USA

Dr. Mingle Gao, Dean, College of Education, Beijing Language and Culture University (BLCU), Beijing, China

Dr. José Gijón Puerta, Professor, University of Granada, Spain

Dr. Mercedes González Sanmamed, Professor, University of Coruña, Spain

Dr. Gabriela Hernández Vega, Professor, University of Nariño, Colombia

Dr. Teresa Langle de Paz, Co-Director of UNESCO Chair on Gender, Wellbeing and Culture of Peace, University of Wisconsin-Madison, USA

Dr. Xiang Long, Guilin University of Electronic Technology, China

Dr. Liliana Morandi, Associate Professor, National University of Rio Cuarto, Cordoba, Argentina

Dr. Joëlle Morrissette, Professor, Department of Educational Psychology, Université of Montreal, Quebec, Canada

Dr. Martha Murzi Vivas, Professor, Univ. of Los Andes, Venezuela

Dr. Thi Cuc Phuong Nguyen, Vice Rector, Hanoi University, Vietnam

Dr. Shirley O'Neill, Professor and Dean, Faculty of Education, University of Southern Queensland, Australia

Dr. José-Luis Ortega, Professor, Foreign Language Education, Faculty of Education, University of Granada, Spain

Dr. Surendra Pathak, Head and Professor, Department of Value Education, IASE University of Gandhi Viday Mandir, India

Dr. Charls Pearson, Logic, Semiotics, Philosophy of Science, Peirce Studies, Director of Research, Semiotics Research Institute, China

Dr. Luis Porta Vázquez, Professor at the National University of Mar del Plata CONICET, Argentina

Dr. Shen Qi, Associate Professor, Shanghai Foreign Studies University (SHISU), Shanghai, China

Dr. Timothy Reagan, Professor and Dean, College of Education and Human Development, Univ. of Maine, USA

Dr. Antonia Schleicher, Professor, NARLC Director, NCTOLCTL Exec. Director, ACTFL Board, Indiana University-Bloomington, USA

Dr. Farouk Y. Seif, Exec. Director of the Semiotic Society of America, Center for Creative Change, Antioch University Seattle, Washington, USA

Dr. Gary Shank, Professor, Educational Foundations and Leadership, Duquesne University, Pittsburgh, Pennsylvania, USA

Dr. Kemal Silay, Professor, Flagship Program Director, Department of Central Eurasia, Indiana University-Bloomington, USA

Dr. José Tejada Fernández, Professor, Autonomous University of Barcelona, Spain

Dr. François Victor Tochon, Professor, University of Wisconsin-Madison, Deep Education Institute, President of the International Network for Language Education Policy Studies, USA

Dr. Brooke Williams Deely, Women, Culture and Society Program, Philosophy Department, University of St. Thomas, Houston, USA

Dr. Jianfang Xiao, Associate Professor, School of English and Education, Guangdong University of Foreign Studies, China

Dr. Dan Jiao, Henan University of Technology, Zhengzhou, China

Dr. Danielle Zay, University of Lille 3 Charles De Gaulle, France

Dr. Ronghui Zhao, Director, Institute of Linguistic Studies, Shanghai Foreign Studies University, Shanghai, China


Other referees may be contacted depending the Book Series or the nature and topic of the manuscript proposed.

Contact: publisher@deepeducationpress.org

## DEEP ACTIVISM
## BOOK SERIES

### Book Series Editors:
### Araceli Alonso and Teresa Langle de Paz

Deep politics could challenge the status quo. Examining everyday gender politics and reconceptualizing the position of the citizen, consider that acting on social representations might help the change process to address social hierarchies and inequalities. Our institutional systems do not tolerate critical examination but rather support conformity, norms, standards and obedience. Everyday politic is grounded in ruled relations. Feminist deep activism, rather than focusing on resisting the reproduction of gender hierarchies, centers on a freedom quest, it initiates a process that can create a new terrain for equality. Thus deep activism links aesthetics with inquiry as a living process. Its commitment to social justice manifests through aesthetics to envision and create alternative imaginaries.

Moral imagination provides the mythic ferment of the future, its inquiry process paints the new possibilities. Dream/critique forms political humanism. What appears crucial is to step for a while outside one's culture to establish an ethical distance vis-à-vis everyday judgment, as conformism is imposed by a culture that uses the instruments of assertiveness to make its claim and produce patriarchal authority, social hierarchies, power centralization, and delineate the margins of cultural acceptability. Feminist deep activism defines a new relationship with the world. It goes together with new, more interactional and open ways of expression. In this process, hope and love constitute non-foundational (i.e. non-universalist) foundations.

## INCLUSIVE EDUCATION AND PARTNERSHIPS

### BOOK SERIES

### Book series editor: Danielle Zay

This collection aims at developing an in-depth understanding of inclusive education as well as its related practices. Inclusive education main principle is anchored in the right to education each citizen, coming from democratic societies, is endowed with. This person can develop to its full potential and live a better life. Biological, psychological, cultural, racial, social differences are not seen as problems meant to exclude but as resources and a wealth for the living together. Inclusive education is conceived so to emphasize the notions of sharing and partnerships. Sharing of ideas, sharing of research results, sharing of practices from partners coming from various fields and various perspectives, all those are seen as most helpful in the understanding of inclusion linked problems, thanks to a systemic perspective. Such a rich understanding will encourage the emergence of innovative solutions most susceptible to adequately meet growingly complex and technologically advanced societies needs.

### INCLUSION THROUGH SHARED EDUCATION

### Danielle Zay[1] and Joanne Deppeler[2] (Eds.)

[1]University of Charles de Gaulle Lille 3, France
[2]Monash University, Australia

This volume gathers data from investigators working in very diverse cultural environments: Australia, Canada, China, Spain, United States of America, France, Great Britain and Taiwan, analyzing the most recent development of a principle of orientation in politics and practices in OECD countries: inclusive education. Responding to the growing number of critics and challenges arising from the reforms of the education system going in the same direction, the authors of this volume study the evolution of this concept.

## DEEP LANGUAGE LEARNING
## BOOK SERIES

Language learning needs to be reconceptualized in two ways: first, as an expression of dynamic planning prototypes that can be activated through self-directed projects. Second, integrating structure and agency to meet deeper, humane aims. The dynamism of human exchange is meaning- producing through multiple connected intentions among language task domains.

Language-learning tasks have a cross-cultural purpose which then become meaningful within broader projects that meet higher values and aims such as deep ecology, deep culture, deep politics and deep humane economics. Applied semiotics will be a tool beyond the linguistic in favour of value-loaded projects that are chosen in order to revolutionize the current state of affairs, in increasing our sense of responsibility for our actions as humans vis-à-vis our fellow humans and our home planet. In this respect, deep instructional planning offers a grammar for action. Understanding adaptive and complex cross-cultural situations is the prime focus of such a hermeneutic inquiry.

# A LIFE IN SIGNS AND SYMBOLS
# BOOK SERIES

## SIGNS AND SYMBOLS IN EDUCATION
## EDUCATIONAL SEMIOTICS
### François Victor Tochon
University of Wisconsin-Madison, USA

In this monograph on Educational Semiotics, Francois Tochon (along with a number of research colleagues) has produced a work that is truly groundbreaking on a number of fronts. First of all, in his concise but brilliant introductory comments, Tochon clearly debunks the potential notion that semiotics might provide yet another methodological tool in the toolkit of educational researchers. Drawing skillfully on the work of Peirce, Deely, Sebeok, Merrell, and others, Tochon shows us just how fundamentally different semiotic research can be when compared to the modes and techniques that have dominated educational research for many decades. That is, he points out how semiotic methods can provide the capability for both students and researchers to look at this basic and fundamental human process in inescapably transformational ways, by acknowledging and accepting that the path to knowledge is, in his words "through the fixation of belief."

In four brilliantly conceived studies, he shows us how semiotic concepts in general, and semiotic mapping in particular, can allow both student teachers and researchers alike insights in these students' development of insights and concepts into the very heart of the teaching and learning process. By tackling both theoretical and practical research considerations, Tochon has provided the rest of us the beginnings of a blueprint that, if adopted, can push educational research out of (in the words of Deely) its entrenchment in the Age of Ideas into the new and exciting frontiers of the Age of Signs. – Gary Shank, Duquesne University.

# LANGUAGE EDUCATION POLICY
# BOOK SERIES

Language Education Policy (LEP) is the process through which the ideals, goals, and contents of a language policy can be realized in education practices. Language policies express ideological processes. Their analysis reveals the perceptions of realities proper to certain sociocultural contexts. LEPs further their ideologies by defining and disseminating the values of policymakers. Because Language Education Policies are related to status, ideology, and vision of what society should be and traditions of thoughts, such issues are complex, quickly evolving, submitted to trends and political views, and they need to be studied calmly. The way to approach them is to get comparative information on what has been done in many settings, which are working or not, which are their flaws and merits, and try to grasp the contextual variables that might apply in specific locations, without generalizing too fast.

Policy discourses and curricula reveal the ideological framing of the constructs that they encode and create, project, enact, and enforce aspects such as language status, power and rights through projective texts generated to forward and describe the contexts of their enactments. Policy documents are therefore socially transformative through their evaluative function that frames and guides action in order to achieve language reforms. While temperance and reflection are required to address such complex issues, because moving to fast may create trouble, nonetheless the absence of action in this domain may lead to systemic intolerance, injustice, inequity, mass discrimination and even, genocidal crimes.

## LANGUAGE EDUCATION POLICY
## BOOK SERIES

### DISPLACEMENT PLANET EARTH
### Plurilingual Education and Identity
### for 21st Century Schools

### K. Harrison, M. Sadiku, F.V. Tochon (Eds.)

Displacement Planet Earth engages an urgent call for action for displaced families—immigrant and refugee—whose children attend school in the host countries of the U.S., Europe, and Australia. The book develops the basis for a model of cultural and linguistic rights for these diverse students living under migration circumstances. The 19 scholars who contributed to this volume offer an in-depth look at these questions. This volume goes a long way in providing rationales and strategies, urging immediate action. Three sections address the conceptual, the policies and programs, and the narratives of experiences for particular groups, providing a spectrum written by international scholars.

Language Education Policies and teachers' practices can help repair the contextual, psychological ideological and social fabric of human lives and societies impacted by misconceptions based on language ideologies and language status that lead to miscommunication, discrimination, social divisions, violence, war, and human struggle; especially for those displaced.

# LANGUAGE EDUCATION POLICY
# BOOK SERIES

## LANGUAGE EDUCATION POLICY UNLIMITED: GLOBAL PERSPECTIVES AND LOCAL PRACTICES

### François Victor Tochon (Ed.)

This book is a first. Language Education Policy is a new field of study that establishes a cross section between educational policy and language policy studies. It inherits from an abundance of intellectual and methodological traditions while opening new perspectives that focus on the interface between policymaking and its enactment in a classroom or an educational setting. The study of the interface between the macro-policy level of the political stage and the micro-policies of education in practice implies a focus on how policy decisions are translated into regulations that affect the lives of people. 21 authors have contributed to this outstanding volume that situates the stakes in the new field of inquiry with examples in 14 countries.

"This essential book shows why language education policy will never work if it is top-down and ignores local contexts and stake-holders. It illustrates the fundamental importance of taking local contexts into consideration and actively engaging and empowering local stakeholders in the development and implementation of all language education policy. A better blueprint for successful language education policy would be hard to find."
– Dr. Andy Kirkpatrick, Griffith University

## OUT OF HAVANA
### Memoirs of Ordinary Life in Cuba
#### Araceli Alonso
University of Wisconsin-Madison

*Out of Havana* provides an uncommon ordinary woman's insight into the last half century of Cuba's tumultuous recent history. More powerfully than an academic study or historical account, it allows us intimately to grasp the enthusiasm, commitment and sense of promise that defined many average Cubans' experience of the 1959 Revolution and the first triumphant decades of the Castro regime. As the story shifts into the final decades of the last century (the 1980s Mariel Boatlift, the so-called "special period in time of peace" [from 1991 to the end of the decade], and the 1994 Balseros or Rafters Crisis), it starts gradually to reveal, with understated yet relentless eloquence, an ultimately insuperable rift between the high-flown official rhetoric of uncompromising struggle and revolutionary sacrifice and the harsh conditions and cruelly absurd situations that the protagonist, along with the majority of Cubans, begin routinely to live out. It is a rare and important document, a unique personal chronicle of an everyday Cuban reality that most Americans continue to know only fragmentarily.

**Dr. Araceli Alonso** is a 2013 United Nations Award Winner for her activism on women's health and women right. Associate Faculty at the University of Wisconsin-Madison in the Department of Gender and Women's Studies and in the School of Medicine and Public Health, she is the Founder and Director of the award-winning non-profit organization Health by Motorbike.

## Other books published by Deep Education Press

- Language Policy or the Politics of Language: Re-imagining the Role of Language in a Neoliberal Society

- Deep Education Across the Disciplines and Beyond: A 21st Century Transdisciplinary Breakthrough

- The Deep Approach to Teaching and Learning World Languages and Cultures: Research on Turkish

- Policy for Peace: Language Education Unlimited

- Science Teachers Who Draw: The Red Is Always There

- Educational Imperialism: Schooling and Indigenous Identity in Borikén, Puerto Rico

- Help Them Learn a Language Deeply Deep Approach to World Languages and Cultures

- Global Language Policies and Local Educational Practices and Cultures

- My Cannibalized Self: An Autoethnography - Biliteracy Development in Japanese Heritage Language Study

- From Transnational Language Policy Transfer To Local Appropriation: The Case of the National Bilingual Program in Medellín, Colombia

- Traditional Potters: From the Andes to Vietnam

- Performing the Art of Language Learning: Deepening the Learning Experience through Theatre and Drama

- Transfer of Learning and the Cultural Matrix: Culture, Beliefs and Learning in Thailand Higher Education

- Family Child Care Relationship-Based Pedagogy: Provider Perspectives on Regulation, Education, and Quality Rating

- Formación y desarrollo de profesionales de la Educación: Un enfoque profundo

# Guide for Authors

What our Publishing Team can offer:

➤ An international editorial team, in more than 30 universities around the world.

➤ Dedicated and experienced topic editors who will review and provide feedback on your initial proposal.

➤ A specific format that will speed up the production of your book and its publication.

➤ Higher royalties than most publishers and a discount on batch orders.

➤ Global distribution through Amazon and Barnes & Noble in the U.S., UK, Australia, Europe, Russia, China, South Korea, and many other countries with Expresso Book Machines, printed in minutes on site for in-store pickup.

➤ Fair recognition of your work in your area of specialization.

➤ Quality design. Using the latest technology, our books are produced efficiently, quickly and attractively.

➤ Dissemination through Deep Education campuses.

➤ Book Series: Deep Education; Deep Language Learning; Signs & Symbols in Education; Language Education Policy; Deep Professional Development; Inclusive Education; Deep Early Childhood Education; Deep Activism.

**Contact:**
**publisher@deepeducationpress.org**

**Deep Education Press**

10657 Mayflower Road
Blue Mounds, WI 53517 USA

**Contact:**

**publisher@deepeducationpress.org**

**Deep Activism Book Series** at DEP

**Health by All Means** at DEP

Correspondence for this volume:
**Araceli Alonso**
aalonso@wisc.edu
**Teresa Langle de Paz**
langledepaz@wisc.edu

CPSIA information can be obtained
at www.ICGtesting.com
Printed in the USA
BVHW061111130920
588707BV00010B/356

9 781939 755438